Every Child Should Have a Chance

♂ ♂ ♡ ♡ ♀ ♀

Leila Daughtry-Denmark, M.D.

Atlanta, Georgia
1982

Third Edition
First printing, 1982
Second printing, 1986
Third printing, 1988
Fourth printing, 1991
Fifth printing, 1994
Sixth printing, 1996
Seventh printing, 1997
Eighth printing, 1998
Ninth printing, 1999
Tenth printing, 2000
Eleventh printing, 2002
Twelfth printing, 2005

Copyright, © 1971, 1982
by Leila Daughtry-Denmark

Manufactured in the United States of America

Order from
Leila Daughtry-Denmark, M.D.
385 Mullinax Road
Alpharetta, Georgia 30201

To the Giver of Life and
those who help to preserve it

♂ ♀

Contents

Contents ix

♂ ♀

Acknowledgments

To my husband, John Eustace Denmark, without whose help and encouragement this book could not have become a reality, I am most grateful. For many years prior to his retirement as a Vice President of the Federal Reserve Bank of Atlanta I regularly accompanied him to New York where he attended a week's banking conference each February. These were working trips for him but for me they were delightful vacations. It was in the quiet and restfulness of a comfortable hotel room, while he was in meetings, that I started jotting down in rough longhand the thoughts and experiences that go into *Every Child Should Have a Chance*. Upon his retirement some eighteen years ago he took on the large task of converting these rambling notes into composition the average layman might read and understand. The book is the finished product of our joint efforts.

I also acknowledge with much gratitude invaluable assistance given by our daughter and her husband, Mary and Grady Hutcherson, in editing, material arrangement, et cetera. Their two sons, Steven and James, although not able to help with the writing, have made their contribution through inspiration one can obtain only from such wonderful grandchildren as they are. The chapter of the book dealing with grandparents reflects both the thoughts and observations of a pediatrician and the feelings of a happy grandmother.

To Mrs. Hill Healan, a good friend, who typed the manuscript in its final form, I am deeply indebted. Finally, I would be remiss if I did not say a word of thanks to the many parents of my patients who, through the years, have urged me to put in book form my philosophies on the subject of rearing children, and also to the good people of Central Presbyterian Church, Atlanta, who have permitted me to work with them since 1928 in their Baby Clinic where every effort is dedicated to the matter of giving the child in our midst a better chance in life.

♂ ♀

Introduction

This is not a medical book, nor is it meant to be a treatise on child care as the term is generally understood and applied. Perhaps it should not be referred to as a book at all but rather as a group of essays dealing with some of the problems, responsibilities, and opportunities that arise in the rearing and training of children. The thoughts and suggestions expressed in the several chapters are based entirely on my observations and experiences covering some fifty years in the practice of medicine, dealing with thousands of children in all walks of life . . . the poor and the wealthy, the weak and the strong, the loved and the unloved, the privileged and the underprivileged.

There is little in the book that has not already been published in some form or other, but I feel that we have to continue saying these things over and over again hoping we may save a child. If only one person is helped, then my time and effort will not have been wasted.

It is not intended that this book should address itself to the medical profession although it is hoped doctors will read it. Primarily it should be of interest to parents and prospective parents. It should be to them in a general sort of way simply preventive medicine, helping them to avoid some of the mistakes and pitfalls many parents encounter in rearing their children.

What do I mean when I say that every child should have a chance? In the broadest sense, the opportunity to grow and develop in keeping with physical and mental capacity, to be healthy in body and soul, so as to enjoy a full, happy and useful life. It means, among other things, that a child should be conceived by parents who have kept their bodies as perfect as possible; should be nurtured in the womb by a mother who will do those things that are good for her unborn child and avoid those things that may be harmful; and, after birth, loved and trained by parents who are willing to put the welfare of the child first in their daily lives.

The term "way of life" is used in more than one chapter of the book. It is admitted that this is an expression of indefinite meaning in general usage and that ever person has a "way of life" whether by design or otherwise. Experience proves that the direction in which a person goes depends to a large extent on the training and leadership he has from birth on through childhood and even after becoming an adult.

When a child is reared in an environment of confusion and uncertainty—without system and good planning—the chances that he will find a happy, meaningful, and productive way of life are lessened. In some instances children are shuttled from one nursery to another, with a minimum of parental love and attention, and trained during the crucial early years by people who are doing the job only for the money they get out of it. What a great mistake this can be! A child needs two loving and dedicated parents to teach him the way he should go and this is vital up to the age of twelve. Ordinarily the average child at that age can begin to find his own way, although he still needs all the help he can get through the teen years if he is to reach his maximum potential.

Paraphrasing Matthew 16:26, What will it profit a parent if he gain the whole world and lose his child? What will a parent give in exchange for a child?

"The rod and reproof give wisdom: but a child left to himself bringeth his mother to shame." Proverbs 29:15.

The greatest need on earth today is parents—parents who want to and will give their children a chance.

Perhaps the title of this book should be "The Price of Dissipation." The word *dissipate* as defined by Webster means: To scatter; to break up and drive off; disperse; dispel; dissolve. To scatter aimlessly or foolishly; as, to dissipate one's energies. To squander. To separate into parts and disappear; to waste away; vanish. To be wasteful or dissolute in the pursuit of pleasure.

Thus we see that the word *dissipate* does not apply solely to the drinking of alcoholic beverages or the pursuit of other types of so-called pleasure. It includes everything on earth that destroys a child's chance and opportunity in life.

Every Child
Should Have
a Chance

♂ ♀

1. First visit to a newborn baby

The first visit to a newborn baby may mean the difference between a stable and well-adjusted child and a child who never knows security and self-reliance. This visit, in my way of thinking, is the most important visit a doctor ever makes to a well patient.

After the mother has read and talked for nine months about the art of rearing a child, she has become confused; and by the time the baby comes, she is actually frightened at the thought of the great responsibility of taking this little baby and preparing him for life. Books and conversations don't agree on how this baby should be handled. Some say self-demand—let this baby tell you what to do. But the mother knows she can't understand what each cry means, and she knows there are hundreds of things that might make a baby cry. Some will say we can tell a hungry cry from the desire to sleep or to eliminate, or a gas pain, but the book, doctor, neighbor, grandparents, or old maid aunt can't explain how the cries differ. The mother must understand that no one can tell her what these cries mean.

So this would be the first big upset. Why does the baby cry? Papa says he is hungry; Grandma says he is hot, or wants water; Auntie says he is wet; the nurse says he wants to eliminate and should have an enema or suppository; and a neighbor says he is spoiled. How could a new mother take this confusion, stay in her right mind and nurse a baby!

Then come the questions: When should the baby be fed? How should he be fed? How much? How many stools should he have a

1

day? What should they look like? How often should his diapers be changed? How should he be bathed? How often? How much should he cry? How should the bed be made? Should the baby sleep in the room with the parents? How much should he sleep? Should he be held while taking the bottle? Should the mother nurse him in bed or sit up while he nurses? Should he nurse both breasts each feeding or just one? How should the baby be burped? What kind of soap should be used in bathing the baby? Should oil or cream be used after the bath? And many more questions—which if answered at the first visit, should cut down on the anxiety, and the number of breast babies would increase and the feeding problems decrease. So on this first visit the doctor should not be in a hurry but should take time to get the new mother on the right schedule. The confidence the young mother has in the doctor is determined at this visit.

If the baby is still in the hospital, it is best to ask that he be brought to the mother's bed for this first examination and, if possible, the father should be present. If the first visit is in the home, it is good to have the father, grandparents, and nurse present. This is also true if the baby is brought to the office. Having the father and grandparents present for the first examination and conference clears up many major problems and gets a number of important questions answered dealing with the matter of preparing a little boy or girl to live a happy life. The mother can tell the father, grandparents, and nurse what the doctor advised, but it always has a better effect if they hear it direct from the doctor and have the opportunity to ask questions.

It is so much better to start a child off right than to have to backtrack and correct something that has started wrong. A habit can be formed in a little baby after three experiences or in doing the same thing three days. If a baby is walked three nights at the same time, he has it fixed; and the parents must continue to walk him or expect to hear him cry. If we start a baby out on a routine we are not willing to follow, the baby suffers, the parents suffer, and what could have been a happy home may become a broken home. Parents must remember that this little baby has come to live with them—not they with him; and they must understand that they are to be the boss. They have been here for twenty or more years, they know the way, and must show this little baby the way. The father is king, the mother is queen, and this little baby is their subject; and as long as he lives in their house, the child must be made to feel that they can protect and supply all his needs, and meet any problems that come up. This training has to start the day a baby is born if it is to work out; and in this day of conflicting advice, it is difficult for a parent to know what to do.

Many times when I meet parents who are in tears with their first baby, I say to them, "You see that little squirrel out there in that tree; she has babies and she has never read a book or been to a doctor—yet she knows just what to do for them. If you will just settle down and think for yourselves, you will find that these problems are not half as big as they seem. All that little squirrel does for her babies is to feed them, keep them clean, warm or cool, and away from people. Maybe it is not quite that simple, but it is not half as complicated as the books, neighbors, grandparents, and doctors would make you think it is."

Having a baby is not a sickness, and it is not necessary for a mother to be treated as a sick person just because she has had a baby. She is not sick although she is tired from carrying extra weight for six months. She has lost some sleep during the last few weeks of her pregnancy, and she should have the right to rest for at least two weeks before going back to keeping house and making the meals. After such a rest she is able to care for the baby, and is much happier if she can do this and let others keep the house and prepare the meals. Nobody can care for a new baby like his own mother, and no mother can be pleased with the way other people care for her baby. These two—mama and baby—should be permitted to live together quietly and have a chance to get acquainted before either has time to get upset.

Too much company and too much talk have been the downfall of many little helpless babies. Mrs. Jones calls, talks for two hours, wears the mother and father out, and just as she leaves she says, "I should not have come over today with this bad cold but I just had to see the new baby." In seventy-two hours the baby has a cold, the mother is so worried she can't eat, the milk is gone . . . and papa loses his temper. This is such a common occurrence that it seems to me people who are sick would learn never to go near a new baby. New babies should not have company, but should be kept quiet and away from unnecessary people until they get a good start. A little baby with a bad cold is a sad sight, and somebody had to give him the cold. He did not enjoy Mrs. Jones' visit for she talked loudly, and his little thin eardrums vibrated at such a high pitch that he dreamed he heard her for nights after she was gone.

The quiet simplicity of rearing a baby cannot be stressed enough in this age of television, radio, telephone and noise from the street and the sky. A little baby should have the right to a quiet life for the first six months until his body can get adjusted gradually to a noisy world. I hear parents say they are not going to make any effort to keep noises down, for the baby has to learn to live with them. That sounds good, but they would see the situation differently if they could only know how loud these noises are to that delicate little eardrum, and how frightened—after having been in a quiet place for nine months—the baby becomes in having these noises appear all of a sudden. This little life that is starting should be permitted to take the shocks gradually. So it is all important that the baby should be treated like the Indians used to treat their babies, or like the cat treats her kittens—he should be hidden away for the first few weeks of life until he can get a good start.

At this first visit it is useless to give the mother a lecture about what she should or should not have done during the nine months of her pregnancy; that is water over the dam. We must make the mother understand that the baby she has must be accepted and that she must take this little baby and make out of him all he is capable of being. If, during pregnancy, she has smoked or dipped tobacco, drunk alcoholic beverages, taken sedatives, hypnotics, tranquilizers—or anything a baby should not have, this mother knows that her baby has had to take all of these as well as other substances she has consumed, and that he is just as much addicted to them as she is and must suffer until the addiction is overcome. This terrible condition is seen often now and, in the case of the addicted baby, doctors spend the first three to four months of his life trying to get him adjusted to normal living.

When we study the animal kingdom, the cat, dog, cow, horse, we never see their little ones having to go through all this torture; their babies are docile, cuddly, happy and quiet. The mother cow would not eat or drink anything that would hurt her calf. The horse on a luscious mountain trail picks her food with the utmost care, never taking any food that would harm her or her foal. Man is supposed to be the wisest of all creatures, yet we see a pregnant woman drinking alcoholic beverages, smoking or dipping tobacco, taking drugs that she would never think of giving to her child; but she is making her unborn baby take these things for nine months. Then she expects her baby to come into the world as happy, docile, and cuddly as a little kitten.

This cannot be, for this little baby is a dope fiend, nicotine addict, coffee addict, alcoholic—or whatever the mother is addicted to; and to be deprived of the drug he has had for nine months makes him a wreck. He is jumpy, cyanotic and stiff; he vomits, spits up, is constipated or has frequent stools, cries, and cannot be consoled until he has time to get over nine months of dissipation. The baby eventually will get relaxed to a certain extent, but he never gets over the psychological and neurological damage he suffers during these first few months. The baby can never be what he could have been if he had not had to dissipate for nine months before he was born. Sometimes a mother has to take a drug to protect her against convulsions, hypertension, and many other conditions that have to be treated to save the mother, but we must remember that the baby is getting everything the mother gets, and it takes time for the baby to get off the drug.

Saying this to a mother on the first visit would be very upsetting, so all that should be said is to remind her that her baby is addicted to whatever she has consumed in the past nine months. If she nurses the baby and discontinues the stimulants or drugs, the shock to the baby will be lessened; but if she does not nurse the baby, she will see within twenty-four hours after he is born that he becomes stiff and irritable and that it will take time for him to get adjusted to a life without the things she has been taking.

She should expect the baby to be nervous, cry a great deal, and be hard to get started on a formula that will stay down or satisfy; and she should understand that it is not the food that is at fault and causing the trouble, but it is the baby's condition.

Many babies get change after change in formula: formulas made weaker, formulas made stronger, cow's milk, goat's milk, then soybean milk—back on cow's milk; but they continue to cry, spit, or have trouble with elimination, and nothing seems to help but time. They are given atropine, phenobarbital, paregoric, and many other drugs to try to clear up this condition caused by the mother's dissipation during her pregnancy. All the formula-changing and drug-taking keeps the mother busy until the baby cures itself with time. I am sure many of these babies have been made worse by drugs and formula-changing.

After the doctor gets a good history on the mother and learns that the baby is addicted to some drug, he can proceed with treatment. Many of these babies get X-ray examinations, with a diagnosis of pyloric spasm, hyper-motility of the stomach, or some such report, with a suggestion that some form of atropine be given. If the addiction is nicotine, I give vitamin B-Complex with vitamin C, one cc. intramuscular twice a week, and have found that it helps; but other than that, I have never used any medication. I have the mother keep the baby on the abdomen and as quiet as possible. Noise or disturbance seems to put these little babies in a tonic state that causes severe pain . . . then they cry . . . and swallow air . . . and have colic. The parents think they are hungry and feed them too often, upsetting their bowels, and then the formula is blamed—and changed.

When the addiction is over, the mother may tell the doctor that the baby was allergic to milk for the first six months but now can take all he wants. No—he was not allergic to milk but in six months was able to take all he wanted. (It is true that many babies are allergic to cow's milk, but these babies do not clear up at four to six months.) The baby just calmed down after he went off tobacco, coffee, hypnotics, sedatives, or any other drug the mother took during pregnancy. The baby is relaxed and the condition clears up.

There are many reasons why a baby could be upset at birth other than addiction through his mother, and all these reasons should be worked out. The trouble could stem from a sickness or a metabolic condition. If the baby is not happy, cuddly, hungry, docile and sleepy, and the results are negative when all the other reasons are worked out, then it may be that the mother has caused her baby to be addicted to her habits. In such case the doctor can say to her, "This baby will have to cry and spit up until he gets over his addiction." If a baby cries, spits up, has abnormal stools, a rash, and will not sleep, there is something wrong; and this wrong should not be covered up by some sedative or antispasmodic, but the reason for the trouble should be found and corrected if possible.

There is always a reason for a child to be unhappy. We don't find the babies of the lower animals going through an adjustment period like human beings. This trouble we have with human babies is brought on to a considerable extent by the parents. I often think about the vast amount of happiness that is lost by both mother and child when a mother does not nurse her baby. This lost art has robbed the human race of something that cannot be replaced, for nursing results in a mother-child relationship that cannot be explained. This relationship is the nearest thing to heaven I know of and I speak from experience.

After some fifty years of helping mothers and fathers with their babies, I have come to the conclusion that breeding is of great importance. We can't expect more in the baby than we find in the mama and papa who made him. I hold that the children of today who are bred well are finer physically and mentally than any children of the past. They don't have to suffer the periods of long sickness and poor diet as has been the case through the ages. Now we have treatments for practically all the ills a human being can have; and those that are bred well can grow up to be strong, healthy parents to produce strong, healthy children.

Poor breeding is far in the lead in this country today; and with all that medical science has done to make a better race, we doctors are working harder and seeing poorer specimens of humanity than ever before. This does not sound good coming from a doctor who has worked for so long at this job of trying to give children a chance. I work in a charity clinic to try to bring children up, and I work in the office to try to keep children up; but there are more going down in my office than I am able to bring up in the clinic. Today we are trying to adjust thousands of children that are the products of dissipation to a world they can be happy in.

A Baby's Sleeping Habits

After the baby has been examined, if possible in the presence of the family, we answer the questions. First, how will the baby sleep and how should the bed be made? The bed or bassinet has a water proof cover over the mattress and, if it is water proof, it is also air proof and would not be comfortable; so four towels should be placed over the mattress, and then covered by a sheet stretched skin tight so it cannot be pulled out. Then a cotton quilted pad should be placed on top of the sheet. The baby should be placed on the pad on his abdomen; then he can breathe through the towels if he sleeps on his face and the air can get to the skin and prevent rashes and overheating. The average mother says the baby is happier on her bed, and it is because she does not have a water proof and air proof cover on her bed.

There should never be free objects like pillows or big stuffed dolls left in the bed, for these might cause the baby to be smothered. The cover should be tight at the foot but not tucked on the sides as a normal baby can make his way over the bed as soon as he is born. As a rule he will move forward until he can touch the head of the bed before he goes to sleep. There is no way of knowing, but perhaps it is because the baby wants to cuddle up to mama and feel secure that he seeks a stable object. Anyhow, it is obvious that he wants to be in contact with something.

How should the baby be placed in the bed? There have been many papers published in medical journals on this subject. Some say on the back, some say on the side, and some say on the abdomen. Here again the mother must think a little for herself. All the talk about how a baby should sleep has been by good medical men and which one is she to follow? She can follow but one, so she should go to the lower animals again and see what the cat, the squirrel, the cow, the horse do with their young; for them there is no trouble deciding how to place their babies. There is no animal on earth dumb enough to place newborns on their backs except man. This little baby has been held tight for nine months and when he is placed on his back, his hands and feet go free and he feels like he is falling. He will grab for help that is not there and become startled. With this shock he takes in a deep breath, swallows air, then has the colic and cries— causing more air to be swallowed—and more colic. When he starts to fall asleep, his arm or foot drops and he is frightened again.

I have been called to see a newborn because he continued to cry, and would find the baby flat on his back, so frightened that he would be in a tremor. I would turn him on his abdomen, and by the time I could be seated and obtain a history, the baby would be asleep. The parents may say the fee for a night call is a high price to pay a doctor just to turn the baby on his abdomen. On his back he reacts like a bug on its back. He is frightened until he learns that when his legs and arms drop, there is something to catch them. On his abdomen he is secure since his hands and feet are always in contact with the bed. The way the baby is placed on the bed means much in teaching him to be a secure person. If placed on his back, he is helpless since he cannot move around over the bed as he does on his abdomen; and he cannot use his neck as he can on his abdomen. On the abdomen he will raise his head and turn it from side to side as soon as he is born if he is normal; and in this way he exercises the muscles in the neck and back and can hold his head up much quicker. If a baby does not hold his head up by the time he is two or three months old, a mother will start worrying.

I have seen many babies that had been kept on their backs who could not hold up their heads at the normal time; and the only reason was that they had not been allowed to exercise their necks and back muscles as they should have. If a baby is on his back, he is helpless; and if he spits up, he could strangle as he cannot turn over to spit out the food; if on his abdomen, the food goes out on the cover and is soaked up.

All babies swallow air the first three months of life and this air causes colic; and if a baby is on his back, the colic is much worse. Anyone who has ever had colic knows the relief he gets when he rests on his abdomen. During the first three months babies will pass gas through the mouth and anus all day and they do not need medicine for this normal condition. When they stop swallowing air, they will stop passing gas; and if the baby is on his abdomen, it is much easier to pass off the gas.

If the baby is kept on his abdomen, his head will always have a good shape. The occipital bone in the back of a little baby's head is not united with the other skull bones yet—and if the baby sleeps on his back, this bone will be forced in and his head will become flat in the back. This will make the child look dumb, but it will not affect him mentally; however, it is a source of embarrassment as he grows old enough to know that his head is shaped like an idiot's. In reality, an idiot would not have a peaked top head if he had not been such a good baby who slept on the back of his head. An idiot can have a very pretty head if his mother keeps him on his abdomen. These things may sound minor, but they are major in the long run. Anything that may influence a child and be a source of embarrassment to him is major and should be avoided.

On the abdomen the mucus that accumulates in the nose and throat comes out on the covers and will not strangle as would be the case if the baby were on his back. Every organ in the human anatomy works better in the prone position. What about his feet? Will sleeping on his abdomen make him have flat feet or clubbed feet? If we examine a baby's feet the minute he is born, we will find that the shape is determined by the way he was held inside the mother. A baby's feet are folded up inside the mother in different ways. There is a position we call the fetal position but the feet, hands and head are not always held exactly in the same way. When the baby is born, the feet can be folded just like they were held inside the mother. Sometimes one foot is folded over the other and one foot will look almost like a club foot, with the other foot forced back to the outer side of the leg. The heel may be forced outward to make the foot look as if it is deformed in the shape of a very flat foot. Then both feet may be folded in and appear clubbed at birth, or both feet may be turned out and appear very flat.

The shape of the feet is determined before the baby is born and no matter how the baby is placed in his bed, the feet will not be made worse. In most cases the feet straighten up with time. On the abdomen the baby will sleep on his knees and if the feet tend to turn out, this position will help to turn them in. Time is the cure for most of these cases, but occasionally there is a foot that will require a special shoe which usually effects the correction needed. Infrequently we see a baby with an anatomically deformed foot that must be cared for by an orthopedist.

The baby should be covered according to the temperature of the room. A grandmother will want to cover him too warmly, as she is getting older and requires more cover; but he should never be covered warm enough to make him perspire, for when he perspires, salts and oil are expelled from the body as well as the water, and the baby cannot feel clean and dry if he gets wet with perspiration.

Bathing the Baby

The mother asks how she should bathe her newborn baby. She should place the baby on his abdomen on a table covered with a thick towel. She will need two bath cloths, a tub of warm water, soap, and a soft towel. With the baby on his abdomen, she should go over the entire body with a damp, soapy cloth, lifting up a.ms and legs one at a time, turning the head from side to side to wash face and head, lifting head up a little to wash the neck, always keeping the baby on his abdomen. After the baby is soaped, the soapy cloth should be put aside, never putting it back in the water and getting the water soapy, for then it would be necessary to get a fresh tub of water. Then all the soap should be washed off with a clean cloth and the baby should be dried with a soft warm towel using a patting motion—never rubbing, as this could injure the skin. A break in the skin could lead to impetigo.

After the baby is washed and dried in this manner, no oil or cream should be put on the clean skin. If oil is put on the skin, the baby will perspire and the perspiration cannot evaporate as it is covered with oil; so the baby will become chilled. This would be like letting the baby sleep in wet clothes, which would be uncomfortable and would cause skin rashes. Also, the chilling effect of the greased body causes a lowering of the white cells in the blood, and that makes the baby more susceptible to infections. Cream makes the skin uncomfortable, and there is no reason to put on anything if the skin is clean. A baby's skin is naturally clean and frequent washing is not necessary, except the diaper area.

I always suggest that the mother keep a bottle of sterile water on the bath table by the bed, and when she changes the baby, she should wet a piece of cotton in this water, wash off the diaper area, and then dry it well. With this procedure we decrease the number of cases of impetigo and fungus infection of the diaper area. These two diseases cause much pain to the baby and great worry to the mother. A large number of the babies that use pacifiers and develop thrush also develop thrush in the diaper area, which is hard to clear up.

The eyes and ears do not need any cleaning other than with the bath cloth. If a cotton swab is used in the ear, wax or other substance that might be in the ear could be forced back to close up the canal and cause trouble. Anything put in the eyes would irritate them and make the eyes more susceptible to infection. Sometimes there is a little mucus that can be seen in the nose that is causing an obstruction, and a small twist of cotton wet in sterile water may be used to get the mucus out; but care should be exercised not to insert the cotton too far. A rubber bulb pump should never be used on a baby's nose as this can cause more trouble than the good accomplished. This will cause the mucous membranes in the nose to swell, preventing the baby from breathing through the nose, keeping him awake and causing the sinuses to close up and get infected. We should do as little to a baby's nose as possible, for crying cleans it out if the baby is on his abdomen.

The vulva should be kept clean with sterile water, using a small piece of cotton and never using a cotton swab which is too hard. Sometimes the labia minora get inflamed and, if they are pressed together in this inflamed condition, they may grow together and cause obstruction to proper urination. If this happens, they should be pulled apart which causes a little pain at the time. If kept clean, this will not happen unless the baby is allergic to something that keeps the vulva inflamed, and in this case the cause should be worked out.

Boys are much easier to keep clean if they have been circumcised. There is no special care; just wash the genitalia as the other parts of the body are washed. If the boy baby has not been circumcised, every effort should be made to keep him clean to prevent infection. To care for the umbilicus, it is best not to bother this cord unless there is some discharge. It should be cleaned with a sterile piece of cotton, never covering the cord with adhesive or any dressing or band, but leaving it open to the air. Sometimes when the cord drops off, the area does not heal properly and there is a discharge. This is caused by a small granuloma that will have to be removed by tying off or cauterizing.

The baby's head is washed every time the baby is washed, and oil should never be used on the head. The important thing is to keep the baby's body clean and put nothing on the body unless something abnormal shows up.

The baby should be kept on his abdomen while being dressed. After the baby is clean and dry, fold the diaper in an oblong manner so that it can be fastened well on both sides; then fold it back to make it short enough to cover the buttocks. Lift up the baby's legs and slip the diaper under the body to reach just below the umbilicus, using the thick or folded part of the diaper under the body; then pull the diaper between the legs and over the buttocks and pin on each side. The diaper can be changed in the baby's sleep in this manner without waking him. When we change a baby this way, he will not object; but on his back he will continue to jump and grab for help. After the baby is diapered, the gown or dress should be crushed up in a small roll to the neck of the dress, then the baby's head should be lifted and the garment slipped over the head, never letting it cover the nose; then the arms should be put in the sleeves and the gown or dress fastened in the back. All baby clothes for the first three months should be fastened in the back.

After the baby is dressed, he should be picked up holding his arms tight to the body and placing the baby on the arm of the mother or nurse, on his abdomen, as if riding the arm with his head at the angle of the elbow. This is the way to carry a baby if we want him to feel secure. In this position there is no glare in his eyes and he can see from the right angle. Now that the baby has been bathed and dressed, he is put back on the bed that has been prepared in the proper manner.

How much should the baby sleep? A newborn baby's sleep causes a great deal of talk and argument, and it has been my observation that the parents and grandparents expect a newborn to sleep all the time. Many newborns do much more crying than is normal. The little addicted babies to which reference has already been made are an example. They are nervous and upset until they get off the addiction so these babies do a lot of crying.

Crying

Then there are some that the mother will not or cannot nurse, that are allergic to cow's milk, or any other kind of milk, who will cry excessively until a food is found they can take. In some cases these babies have skin allergies that cause them to itch and sting, making them cry and stay awake. Some are hurt at birth and cry and stay awake more than is normally the case; some are kept too warm; or it could be that some are kept too cold; and some are greased with oil and are uncomfortable. Some babies are born that are not wanted, and they seem to know at birth that they are rejected. They are never happy and do not sleep well. Then comes the most common cause for crying: they are put on their backs and are frightened.

When we eliminate all of the above reasons for crying and not sleeping, we have to remember that every baby is made up differently from every other baby and their ability to respond to pleasure or pain is as different as in adults. So what would make one baby cry might not bother another at all. We cannot say just how much a baby should cry or sleep, but crying is a very important part of a baby's development. Babies must cry and cry hard to open up their lungs to full capacity. A premature, a Down's Syndrome baby, a baby that is injured at birth, or a very weak baby may have trouble expanding his lungs to the normal capacity. So crying is very important. I say to mothers, "If you don't let this baby cry today, he may make you cry tomorrow." A normal baby should cry from three to four hours out of the twenty-four hours in the day for the first three months of his life. In a short time this crying period will take on a definite pattern and can be predicted almost to the minute.

The baby can't sleep all the time, and during the four hours he is awake he starts fussing. When he fusses, he swallows air and gets the colic; and then he cries and swallows more air and has more colic— a vicious circle but a very normal condition and a very healthful condition. For instance, if a baby cries every night after the ten o'clock feeding until two in the morning, then falls asleep, eats well at each four-hour interval, sleeps until the next night at ten o'clock and then cries until two, the parents can rest assured that the crying is not from some abnormal cause but is the crying every normal baby should do.

This crying should not be stopped by giving sedatives or dope. Walking and rocking will not stop the occurrence of this normal crying, but walking or rocking will help the baby to form a habit that the parents will not like. Sedatives or dope will make the baby sick, so the best thing to do is to keep the baby awake from two o'clock until six o'clock in the afternoon for three days, and the crying period can be changed to the daytime hours when crying doesn't sound half so bad as at night. Parents must learn that the crying of a baby is his way of telling them that he is unhappy. And the child must learn at an early age that his crying cannot get for him things that are not good for his physical or mental development.

So the baby should be expected to cry some every day for the first three months because he has swallowed air and has developed colic to make him hurt enough to make him cry enough to open his lungs and give him the required amount of exercise. If parents cannot stand to hear the normal baby cry, it would be better for them to take something to put themselves to sleep than to give the medicine to the baby and make him sick. We must know well that babies cannot sleep all the time; and we must love them enough to hear them cry if it is necessary for their normal development and training. Every child has a different sleep pattern, and the amount of sleep necessary for one would not be enough for another. There are babies who will cry some every four hours and will not do all the day's crying at one time. When these babies are fed to stop the crying, they begin to spit up and have digestive trouble. Then the crying and staying awake may become an all-day and all-night problem. The more often the baby is fed, the more he cries because his stomach is not empty when new food is added, making proper digestion impossible, and resulting in a very distended and painful stomach.

If the baby is kept on his abdomen, with the room cool and the air free from tobacco smoke or gases, and is given the right food at the proper intervals, the parents should not worry about the amount of sleep he gets; for if the environment and the health are good, the baby will get enough sleep. As a rule, a normal newborn will sleep from ten o'clock in the evening until six o'clock in the morning, then take his bottle or breast and go back to sleep until nine when he gets his bath and is fed at ten; then back to sleep until two, then fed. After this feeding, the baby should stay awake and fuss or cry until six o'clock. From six until ten he may fuss or cry some or just stay awake; and at ten he should be fed and off to sleep for the night.

Feeding the New Baby

How much food should the baby take? The amount of food taken and digested is just as varied in babies as the amount of sleep needed. It is not the amount they take, but it is how they digest what they take that matters. One newborn baby may take one ounce and be happy, another may take four ounces and be happy; and both babies may gain the same amount of weight. The manner in which their food is metabolized and assimilated determines how they will gain and be satisfied.

The stomach is a small sack and the food has to remain in the stomach and be mixed with the hydrochloric acid and pepsin and be digested before it is expelled into the gut to be mixed with the bile and pancreatic juices. After this process of digestion, the food is absorbed to supply the needs of the body. If we continue to add milk to the stomach without giving the milk that is in the stomach time to be digested and expelled, the stomach has to expand more and more because the stomach does not expel milk into the gut until it has been digested in the stomach. With the constant adding of milk, there would never be a time when all the milk in the stomach would have gone through the process of digestion; but the old would be mixed with the new. The only thing that could happen would be for the stomach to expand to accommodate all that was put in, or the undigested milk would have to be passed into the gut, or the baby would have to spit up to get relief.

So we see that feeding a child every time he cries would create a serious problem. I have found that demand feedings are very bad. The advocates of demand feeding are trying to simulate the mother of a hundred or more years ago who did not watch a clock in the care of her child. In order to simulate that mother, we would have to also simulate her way of life. A mother of that day had to have a system. She cooked on a stove that had to be fired, she had to make the clothes for the family, do all their baking, get the food and prepare it. Women were too busy to stop every time the baby cried and fix a bottle or nurse the baby.

These people had a perfect schedule and they did not need to look at the clock to see when to feed the baby. They had to get up early to get all their day's work done so they were up before the sun and they nursed or fed the baby before preparing breakfast. After fixing the family breakfast and cleaning up the kitchen, the baby was nursed. Then after doing the housework and fixing lunch, the baby was nursed and then again at bedtime. This schedule was determined by circumstance, not by choice. The baby was happy because he knew this schedule and he expected to eat at a given time. The only way for any animal or man to be happy and secure is to know, and unless there is a schedule, neither man nor animal can know. Security comes only with knowing.

After studying the emptying time of the stomach through X-ray, we see that the four-hour interval seems to be perfect for the baby on cow's milk, and for human milk alone three hours seems to be the perfect time. Cow's milk has ten times as much calcium and phosphorus as human milk, which neutralizes the hydrochloric acid and slows down digestion requiring a longer time. When cereal, meat, vegetables, and fruit are added, the emptying time is longer. At that time the stomach seems to take five and one-half or six hours. It does not matter how much babies take at the time if it is human milk, so long as they make the proper gains in weight and are happy. With cow's milk, goat's milk or milk substitutes, as long as the dilution is right, they can take as much as they want; and unless the baby is sick, he seems to know just how much to take.

If a baby is in pain, he may take more than he should because he thinks sucking will stop all pain. So we must be sure the milk is diluted properly and is warm and the nipple cut so the milk comes easily. (This should be a cross cut one-sixteenth inch both ways.) The baby should be held in the mother's arms snugly and when the baby pulls, she should pull back on the bottle so he can strip the milk out as he does on the breast. The breast is elastic and when the baby pulls, the breast pulls and the baby strips the milk out. If the nipple is placed in the baby's mouth and not pulled as he sucks, he has to mash the milk out and he does not get the proper sucking act. It should not take a baby more than fifteen minutes to take a bottle; and the longer he sucks, the more air he swallows through his nose.

If the baby is small and weak, one might think he should be allowed to nurse for a long time, but that is not true. The smaller and weaker babies are the ones that should not be worn out with long feeding periods. The longer they suck, the more air they swallow and the more colic they have. So the feeding period should be carried out right and should not be haphazard. A baby at the breast or bottle learns the importance of mother and this should be the happiest time of the day for mother and baby; it should always be quiet—never in a rush.

The feeding should never be forced and the mother should not be over-anxious. If the baby is well, he might refuse a complete feeding at times or take a small amount which does not matter for he can wait until the next feeding when he will take enough. So it all comes down to this: maintain a good four-hour schedule, have the food prepared properly, be happy at feeding time, and have patience. The food should never be made too concentrated just because the baby cries or will not take much. As I have said, cow's milk has about ten times as much calcium and phosphorus as human milk and this has to be used or excreted. If the formula is made too concentrated, there is a problem with the fats; so a concentrated formula may create many bad problems. I would never make a formula more concentrated than human milk and never feed closer than four hours.

Many complaints start with a casual method of feeding. The baby never knows when he will eat and the same is true of his father. Papa late for work, mama over-worked, and the thing that should bring the greatest happiness on earth—a baby in the home—brings unhappiness and conflicts between the parents.

How much should the baby gain each day or week? It is not best to weigh the baby each day, for the gain is not a regular daily gain; but he should be weighed at the end of each week. The average baby will gain seven ounces a week. Some breast fed babies will gain much more than that and some will not gain that much. The thing to watch for is a gradual gain and a happy baby. This one-ounce-a-day gain will continue for three months and then the gaining is not so fast—about one-half ounce a day until the baby is six months old.

Then there is a gradual decrease in weight gain and at twenty-four months it has slowed down to three pounds a year, which will continue until age six.

If the baby does not gain gradually, there is something wrong with the food or the baby and this problem should be solved as soon as possible. Just because a baby does not cry when he does not gain is no reason why a parent should not be concerned. A baby can be sick and not cry. If a baby does not gain, there is something wrong with the formula or something wrong with the baby's capacity to digest or assimilate the food, and this should be worked out. The baby should never be forced to eat and never fed a formula that is too concentrated or fed too frequently just because he will not take much at the time and does not gain weight. Two wrongs will not make a right but may make a sick baby. Forced feeding creates one of the biggest problems in pediatrics today. Eating should be a privilege, not a task. We should never try to force our children to eat, sleep or eliminate; but they should be taught from birth that these acts are a privilege and not a task.

The fat baby is not always the healthy or happy baby, so parents should not want their baby to be fat but just to make a gradual gain. Small parents as a rule produce small children and we should not make our children hate themselves if they look like us.

How often should the diaper be changed? If a baby is sleeping well and he is wet or even has a stool, he should not be disturbed until he wakes or at feeding time. Babies develop bad habits by being disturbed too much. Unless a baby is getting something he is allergic to, being wet or having a stool that is not removed immediately will not make the diaper area red or sore; but if the baby is allergic to something he is getting or to the cleaning product in the diaper, even though the diaper is changed often, he will still have trouble with so-called diaper rash.

The baby with so-called diaper rash has an allergy to something he is getting or something the diapers are washed with, or a fungus. After he gets the rash, he may develop impetigo or other infections in the rash. We see babies in the clinic who are not changed often; and when they are changed, the mother may hang the diaper up and let it dry without washing. The diaper is not washed until the baby has a stool, yet many of these babies have no evidence of the so-called rash. So the diaper rash is not necessarily due to dirty diapers or too little changing, but is due to some allergy. The urine and stool act as irritants and we get Monilia, staphylococcic infection, or many other kinds of infections in the eczema caused by the allergy.

A baby should be kept clean and if the baby is awake, a wet or dirty diaper should be changed. Nothing should ever be put on the diaper area unless it is being treated for something. We do much harm to babies by putting on all kinds of oil, cream, and powder. Sterile water seems to be the best treatment to keep the diaper area well.

Should the baby sleep in the mother's room? I am sure babies have slept with their mothers from the beginning of time and I am sure a baby loves to sleep close to his mother's warm body, but times have changed. The mother of today would be afraid of rolling on the baby, and she would not sleep if the baby were in her bed. It is best to have a separate bed for the baby near the mother's so she can see and touch the baby without getting out of bed. It makes the mother and baby feel more secure if they are close together for the first three months. Then the baby and mother are ready for expansion, and some mothers are ready for the baby to be put in his own room if there is an open door between them.

How should the light be in the room? If the baby is on his abdomen, the light will not bother much but a young baby seems to object to a bright light. The light seems to hurt the baby's eyes and it is best to keep the bright lights shaded for at least the first three months, after which the baby will take the light the same as the parents. If the light is kept on at night for many nights, the baby learns to sleep in the light and objects to the dark. So it is best not to start keeping the light on unless it is planned to be continued.

At what temperature should the baby's room be kept? For the first three weeks, if it is winter time, the room should be kept at sixty degrees or above so that if the mother has to get up, the room will not be too cold. If the baby is well and properly trained, after three weeks he can have a room opened at night like the parents are accustomed to having it. All children sleep better in an open room. This does not mean a room where there is a draft, but the temperature in the room may be like the outdoors. The cover should be according to the weather. It is better to dress a baby warm to sleep than to keep the air in the room warm. After three weeks, it is best for the baby to be out in the open a portion of the day. For this, the baby should be dressed according to the temperature. If the baby is kept in the house and the temperature is seventy degrees as it should be, never warmer, the baby should not wear a heavy shirt but should be dressed in a cotton sweater which should be removed as the house warms up.

A mother should always dress her baby a little cooler than she is dressed. It is easy to keep a baby too hot especially if there is a grandmother in the house. Older people seem to think the baby must have a lot of cover. If a baby perspires at all, he is too hot and will not be as happy as he should be. An overheated or overdressed baby as a rule is a sick baby.

How many stools should a baby have a day? That depends on the milk or milk substitute the baby gets—if the baby is not sick. If the baby is on breast milk, there may be two extremes. If the mother's milk is low in butter fat and she is not eating anything the baby is allergic to, the baby may not have a stool each day, but, in many cases, only every third or fourth day. Then when the stool comes, it will be a mustard yellow, thin, not formed, very smooth with no white particles or mucus, and thin enough to soak up in the diaper. A baby of this type gains fast and is happy, but this is the baby that is sometimes subjected to all kinds of treatment that makes him sick—enemas, suppositories, laxatives, catnip tea, too much prune juice, and many other things that upset him.

If the baby is on the breast and is happy, the parents should not worry if there are no stools for three to four days. If the mother eats nuts, chocolate, cream, dressing, or any other very rich food, the baby may have six to eight stools a day which will be green or greenish yellow, very thin with a large amount of mucus and strings, filled with white lumps that look like curds, and the baby's anus will get red and may bleed. The large amount of fat acts as a laxative, which increases peristalsis, and the stool is expelled before the normal re-action of the stool contents is reached, blistering the skin of the buttocks. This is a condition that is often treated as diarrhoea with all kinds of medicines being given which make the baby sick. If the mother leaves off the rich food, the condition clears up. A mother taking food the baby is allergic to may cause a similar condition, but the stools in this case will be yellow and thin but too frequent; and also the anus may get red and bleed.

If the baby is on a formula of cow's milk, goat's milk, or some milk substitute, the baby should have at least one stool a day and not more than three. They should be yellow, soft, formed stools that will shake off the diaper. If they are light yellow and foamy, the formula contains too much fat. If they are thin, watery and yellow, or green, the food is wrong or the baby is sick. If a mother is in doubt about the type of stools the baby is having, she should let the doctor see the stools before treating the baby for a sickness.

How much should the baby be held? New mothers are talked to and advised both in a serious manner and in a joking manner about holding the baby and rocking the baby. My own child had thirteen rocks every night before going to bed with a few lines of a song sung in a monotone way. We started this as soon as we left the hospital and she always loved that time of day and we loved it more. It was a good time to cuddle her and get her in a good mood for a night's sleep. She always expected to have this little period and experience before getting off to bed for the night.

Rocking, singing, holding cannot hurt if it is done consistently and with love. Where the trouble comes with so many babies is that the parents are willing to start a habit with a baby and then get angry with the baby if he demands the rocking, holding, or singing when the parents are tired or have something they would rather do than to continue the little established habit the child has learned to love. That is the breaking of a child when he finds that he can't depend on his parents at all times. If we start a habit, we must not get angry if the child demands that we keep it up. Parents should write the word "Consistency" on every wall in the house if they are to develop a happy, secure child.

This first visit boiled down is this. The mother should be assured that having a baby is not a sickness; that she is able to handle the baby and look after him, and the help she needs is for the housework, laundry and food preparation. The mother should live close to the baby and know what is going on at all times. She should cuddle the baby and keep him swaddled and on his abdomen until he gets adjusted to having his hands and legs free; she should feed the baby on a good schedule; keep the environment quiet without too much light; never let anyone with a cold come near the baby; and have as little company as possible for the first three weeks. The mother should have plenty of time to read, rest, eat and sleep. She should listen to all the advice of family and neighbors and then do as she knows best, never taking seriously all the suggested things that might happen to the baby.

She must think for herself and build the type child she wants. This is her chance and she should have free rein and not be dominated by parents or in-laws. The parents and in-laws should say, "We are going to treat this mother like we wanted to be treated when we had our children." Caring for a newborn is a great pleasure if that newborn baby is normal and is wanted.

After the doctor sees the baby in the hospital and goes over all of the above matters with the parents, the baby will not be seen or checked again until he is brought to the office at three months of age. Of course, if there is illness or some special reason why the parents think the doctor should see him, they should bring him in.

♂ ♀

2. The stages in the life of a child

From Birth to Two Years

When a baby is born, he is cuddly and fits the outside of the mother's body as well as he did the inside of her body. When she holds him on her chest, his little body fits her chest and his head finds a perfect contour pillow made by her neck and clavicle. At nursing time her arm makes a hammock that is secure and this little newborn is satisfied with only two things—his mother and his food.

A pat from the mother, or a song, or some bouncing on her knee, or a few rocks by her in an old-fashioned rocking chair can quiet this little life quicker and better than any sedative or narcotic that has ever been made. It is a case of mother needs baby and baby needs mother, and one can't be happy without the other. This mother-baby relationship is one life, and there has never been a love on earth to compare with it. I am talking about the normal mother with a normal baby who was made of good seed and was grown in good soil.

Not all newborn babies react like the above for the reason that some were made from a sperm that was created and grown in the body of a glutton, or on too much alcohol from an alcoholic, too much nicotine from a chain smoker, too much caffeine from a nervous wreck, too much phenobarbital or other things a man may take to make his body imperfect. This sperm helped to make up the seed that is to make a new life and a great deal depends on that sperm— something that is not talked about a lot in breeding human beings, but seems to be most important in the breeding of cows, horses, or other animals.

A man will pay a great sum of money for a male animal to improve his herd, but he will marry his daughter off to a man who has a body that has been made inferior by dissipation, that will in turn make inferior the bit of protoplasm that will go into the making of his offspring. If this dissipated man is married to a dissipated woman and the ovum has had the same kind of environment, this little new baby has two strikes against him already; and if he has to spend nine months in the body of a dissipating mother who continues to drink, smoke, take too much coffee, take drugs or who overeats, his situation becomes all but hopeless. A baby born under these circumstances does not have an equal chance, but is condemned at birth. Now this kind of baby does not cuddle, and is not the baby I am talking about.

The normal baby will cuddle close to his mother as a little kitten cuddles and will eat, sleep, and cry the normal amount each day; and that is about all he wants to do for the first three months. Then he begins watching his mother's face as she talks, and as she moves her mouth and raises her eyebrows, he will do the same thing. Then he begins to carry on a cooing conversation with his mother and he seems to understand all she says; he smiles when she smiles, and cries when she looks angry.

At three months he still wants to be close to his mother's body and held tight. He likes to be talked to and sung to. He is dependent on her for everything.

At six months the baby begins to crawl, but he wants to be in his mother's presence. She can sit and sew for hours with the baby happy on a pallet but when she leaves the room, the baby will cry. This is annoying to a mother who does not understand the stages in a child's life but the crying is a compliment to her, showing that she and the baby have a normal mother-baby relationship. The baby is happy at nursing time and feeding time is a pleasure; he likes to eat and the mother likes to see him eat.

The complete dependence on the mother continues to grow more and more evident until the baby is a year old; he likes to be fed by her, dressed, bathed, carried in her arms, rocked, talked to, and played with. The mother can make the baby laugh, wave by-by, do a pat-a-cake, or do anything she tells him to do. At one year a baby likes to please his audience. A normal baby at one year of age with a normal mother is the best example of true happiness on earth. If a baby is born well and has a mother who loves him enough to nurse, hold, rock, sing, speak quietly and kindly, he has learned the greatest lesson of love and security.

The period of the child's being completely dependent on the mother—and enjoying it—begins to show evidence of breaking about the eighteenth month. The little fellow wants to hold the spoon and feed himself and begins to show a temper if he can't. About the twenty-fourth month he wants to put on his clothes and do everything for himself and, if not allowed to do for himself, he may have a temper tantrum. He is very independent now, puts his heels in the ground, and will not be pushed around. Every command gets a "no" and he means no. If we tell him to eat, he will not; and if we tell him he can't eat, he will cry until he gets it.

At two years every normal child begins to live a negative life. He rebels at every command and this will last for four years or until he learns the value of obedience. Because of the feeding problems that arise at this age, this stage in the life of a child is dealt with at some length in the next chapter dealing with the feeding of children. At this stage is a parent's great opportunity to teach these important lessons: honesty, truthfulness, love, fair play, health habits, parental authority, respect for elders, good manners, and many other lessons that will prepare him to be ready to meet life out of the home when he is six. From two to six he is braver than he will ever be. He is brave enough to try anything, so that makes this period in his life the most important teaching period.

If the laws of life are taught well at this period, we have a good foundation on which to build a man or woman. The teaching during this period should be done by the parents and grandparents. If a Smith wants to grow a Smith, a Smith must teach a Smith how to be a Smith from birth to six years of age. An overworked statement by mothers who don't want to take this great responsibility of training a child in this negative period is, "My child needs to be with other children. He is too much of a mama's baby, and I need to get away from him."

All this is an excuse to get out of this great responsibility and tedious job of teaching a negative child how to live. The reward that comes to a mother who has spent six years teaching her child a good way of life is the greatest reward on earth. A child who has not had this basic training finds life a big problem. The teacher, preacher, schoolmates, and social worker try later to teach these laws of life but the period when they could have been taught with ease has passed, and now the child must learn the hard way.

From Two to Twelve

From two to six, the teaching process requires love, patience, consistency, example, time, prayer—but the pay-off is great. The period from six to twelve in a child's life is like a beautiful oasis in a desert after passing through the negative period from two to six, when all the answers are no and the appetite nil. To see a child hungry and obedient is wonderful; and that is what happens at six if the child has been trained well up to that age.

Checking children for school at age six has won me much praise I did not deserve. Mothers will come back after the school check-up and say, "Doctor, I don't know what you did to little Johnny, but he has gained so fast since he started to school—his appetite has increased, and he has never been so good. I don't know what has happened to him; he has changed so much; he is so kind and thoughtful; maybe it was starting to school."

At six a child begins to eat well; in fact, he eats twice as much as he did from two to six, and he gains weight and height. He is kind to animals and his playmates, he will take turns, will share his toys, is ambitious, and anxious to learn. He comes into the church. He gets interested in scouting, likes to build, talks about what he would like to do as a man and is interested in his health. If a child has been trained right from birth to six, then from six to twelve is the easiest, the most pleasant, the happiest, and the most rewarding period in his life. The child has learned how to live during the negative period and has passed the period of frequent colds. In most cases he has had the usual childhood diseases.

From six to twelve is the period in a child's life when parental suggestions and advice are best accepted and followed. During this period a child will listen and ask questions and wants help in his plans; he likes to work with his parents and have his parents work with him. At this period parents can make suggestions and create interest in the better things of life. If a child at this period shows an interest in a subject that would be good for him, he should be exposed to this subject as much as possible. If the interest would not lead to something good for the child, the parents should take time to explain to him what an interest in this subject would lead to, for at this age a child will listen and learn. At this age, parents should do all they can to expose their children to the best possible way of life, art, music, nature, science, church, school, perfect home, love of their homeland and the flag, to open their eyes to the beauties of this world. At this age they want to work for money, and no job seems too hard; they will cut grass, carry papers, and carry bags in the grocery store. They want to own things, have dogs, cats, horses, tree houses, boats, a way to ride; they want to have their own room.

The normal boy and girl from six to twelve like to please and like to listen to their elders talk. They are collectors of stamps, shells, snakes, frogs, coins, and their room walls may be covered with pictures of ball players or presidents. At this age you may find a boy's or girl's room filled with what parents call trash, but to this young person every small item is important and should not be misplaced or spoken of lightly.

The chief examples a child has the first six years of life are his parents and grandparents. He learns a way of life, which may be good or bad, but we can't argue with a little boy six years old about his way of life; for what his parents have taught him he believes is right. So all of these six-year-olds meet in a common school, and are ready at this age to practice what they have learned in their homes. They are ready to see if the training they have had will work outside the home. When my child started to school, she had learned a way of life; and it was interesting to hear her ask why other children behaved as they did. One night at supper she said, "Mama, the teacher had us answer some questions about our home life . . . if we washed our teeth . . . ate with the family . . . what time we went to bed; and do you know Jean stays up until ten o'clock and I go to bed at seven! I want to stay up tonight."

I said, "All right, you may, but the reason I like for you to go to bed early is because you will feel like getting up early and have breakfast with us and be ready to go to school. If you go to bed that late, you will have to sleep late; and you would not see Papa before he goes to work. You may try it tonight." About eight o'clock I noticed she was very quiet and it was not long before she said, "I wish Papa would go up with me and put me to bed."

How he dresses, eats, talks, works, spends, saves. Thousands of these questions come up when a child starts to school. Every day he has to make decisions as to whether his way of life is really best or whether the way his friends and schoolmates behave is best. At that time the child begins to question his parents as to why they live as they do and not as the child was taught to live. Parents must be ready with a reason if they hope to make their child secure. In a world with so many different ways of life there must be a reason why Papa pays his debts and his friend Johnny's papa does not. There must be a reason why Papa drinks and smokes, claiming it is all well and good, while the teacher says it is bad to do these things that harm his body and make it less efficient.

Mama must explain to her daughter that the body she has must be kept well and free of dissipation as some day it is to be the home and maker of the next generation, and that Mary's mother is wrong when she teaches Mary by example that it is right to smoke and drink. This period from six to twelve is the time to teach because it is the time the child is willing to listen. The answer to a question doesn't suffice if it is simply, "You can't do that because it is wrong." No, that answer is not good for children in this age group because they want to know the reason for things. Why a thing is wrong must be given along with the answer.

A child should be taught at this period to analyze every question that comes up in this manner: Would this act make my body and life better or worse? Would this act hurt another human being or thing? Am I doing as I would like to be treated? Is this an act of a man or a coward?

In groups of girls and boys at this age there is much discussion and many of the children, who have not had homes in which there are definite standards or an established way of life, can be expected to feel insecure. At this age children need to be in close contact with their parents, and they must feel free to discuss any subject with their parents. If a child has been taught that the parents will listen to his questions, no matter how small or personal they may be—and will keep his secrets, the child will come to the parents with his problems and let them guide him as he seeks to decide between right and wrong. There should be time and patience with all questions; and the answers should show the child what the end results would be with a certain act.

Teachers who instruct children at this age should be of the highest type. They should be an example for the child to live by. A child in this age group has more admiration for his teachers than at any other age in the entire educational period and in many instances will listen to the teacher's reasoning in preference to that of the parents. When we select teachers for our schools—those who are to teach from the first grade through the sixth—we should select the type people we would like our children to use as models for their lives. We cannot stress this too much. I am sure that the teacher in this period of a child's life has been the making or breaking of many children. A teacher should never try to work with this age group if he does not have uppermost in his mind the responsibility he bears in shaping the lives of these little people, for they put much confidence in what the teachers do and say. Teachers, as well as parents, must help all they can during this six years of a child's life when the child is so anxious to find all the reasons for things and when his mind is receptive to reasons. They should never be taught by word or example a way of life or a reason for life that would not be good for them or for the world in which they live.

This period is the time a mother-daughter relationship must be formed. It must be made by the time the girl is twelve or it cannot be made at all. Mother and daughter should have a great deal of time together. The same is true of mother and son, father and son, father and daughter. We cannot stress this relationship too much; for if the parent and child have not established the right relationship from six to twelve, there is always trouble from that point on; there is no period so important as this to save the adolescent.

Adolescence

Adolescence is the period in the life of a human being that has been the most talked about, written about, and worried about as far back as we have any recorded writing or history. Socrates spoke about how the adolescent in his time misbehaved and showed great concern over what might become of the younger generation. We read the same story about the adolescent in the Old and New Testaments. It is a big and important subject and a period through which every adult has had to pass. When we see so many great and noble adults, it should take some of the fear out of the parents who see their child approaching this period; and they should be comforted by the fact that the majority of children do not go down at this period.

Why has this period of human life been one of such great dread and worry to parents, teachers, preachers, doctors, law makers and law enforcers? First, at this age a child comes to the point in life when the parents cannot completely dominate. Up to this time in the life of a child who has been reared by good parents, the child has been willing to let the parents rule as king and queen. His physical body is small in comparison to the parents, and he feels the need of a protector; and his parents have been that protector for twelve or more years.

At adolescence, human beings are neither adults nor children; they do not fit into either group. They have the minds of children and the desires of adults. They want to be free to run their own lives but they are not mentally or physically mature enough to do that. They have to be continually reminded that when two people marry, build a home and have children, the parents are the king and queen in that kingdom—and must reign supreme—and the children in that home must love, respect, and obey as long as the parents provide the home and the money that pays for their keep. Then when the children are mentally and physically able to go out and make their own home, the parents will grant them the right to a home like they have had and will not interfere with the way they run their home.

If adolescents get this picture, as a rule they begin to think and adjust their lives to this way of life. I have parents come to me with their adolescent problems who will make this statement, "As long as they stay in my house, they have got to do what I say." That is the way it should be, but that statement can't make it so. It is best to say to your adolescent, "Now, son (or daughter), you should never do or say anything in our home that you would not want your son or daughter to do or say in your home."

I find that many parents are actually afraid of their adolescent children. They are afraid to command or even suggest things for them to do for fear they will get upset. When adolescents find that the king and queen in their kingdom cannot rule, they take over and that is when the kingdom falls because the children are not mentally or physically ready to reign. Parents must never speak to a child in a way they would not like to be spoken to and when they command or make a statement, they must carry through if the child is to respect them.

At adolescence the child seems to be the most sensitive to good or bad, right or wrong. Young people feel this and get very disturbed. Thousands of rebellious thoughts come into the adolescent's mind, such as: Why don't you go out and do as you please? Don't be a mama's boy. You are old enough to think for yourself. Education is not everything. Try out these things that adults do. You have a right to drink and smoke if you like. You have a right to have a car. You should not let people tell you when to come in.

Parents must take time to explain to these young people that this is nothing new, but these thoughts and suggestions have been happening to adolescents since the beginning of time; and that at this time in their lives they have to learn to take each suggestion made by the devil and study it out and decide for themselves what they will do with the suggestion made. That is what makes adolescence such a big problem.

Up to this time children are willing to accept help from the parents in making decisions, but now at adolescence they feel they should do it themselves. They play the part of an adult and do the things that will make them appear as adults and when the devil makes the suggestion so attractive, it is difficult for an immature adult to decide what to do.

If he is not helped by the parents, doctor, preacher, and teacher to understand these suggestions and the source of these suggestions, the child may become a juvenile delinquent. The parents must say to this young person. "There is a great fight for you between good and bad, and you are the only person on earth who can decide which force will control you—good or bad." Young people should be made to see that this time in their lives is one when they are the only persons held responsible for their acts by man or God. They may try to use their parents, school, church, and environment as an excuse for their acts, but it will not work. They are now old enough to decide whom they will follow: God or the devil.

Parents must know that at adolescence there is a great change in the glandular system in these young people. They gain pounds in a few months and they may grow several inches in a year. In a year's time there has to be a complete change in the type of clothes, and the shoe size may go up two to four numbers. It takes time to get adjusted to this size change. They are called lazy, clumsy, and gluttons. They are not lazy but are really tired, for it takes time to develop strength sufficient for them to carry all the new weight. They must not do too much resting as they cannot then develop the strength they need, but they must have some interest that will keep them active until the body is strong enough to work without so much effort. They are clumsy because they have to learn how to use this big body. In boys the feet seem to just kick up the rug or hit the table leg and upset the water. It takes a long time to get this big body adjusted to graceful living. They are not gluttons; it takes a great deal of food for this large body so the parents have to learn a new way of cooking to supply the adolescent's needs.

These young people need help—not criticism. I am sure that every juvenile delinquent has been made to feel like a nobody by somebody he loves. When a child finds that his parents don't have any confidence in him, he feels he is given free rein. If the parents, teacher, doctor, law maker, and law enforcer let young people find out they have no confidence in them, then they have nothing to live up to.

The mother of one of my patients called one day crying. She had been a perfect mother and had developed a son who was as nearly perfect as any boy could be. She said, "Doctor, I am heartbroken; I want to talk to you." I asked her what the trouble was. "I would rather come out to your office and talk there," she answered. She came over and we had the following conversation.

"You know we have tried our best to train our son by example, and now he is sixteen and he has changed so much I can't believe he is my son," she said. "Give me an example of what you are talking about." "He will tell a lie." "No—you can't use that word against that fine boy I have had as a patient for sixteen years; let's soften that statement a bit. You mean he does not tell you the truth. The word 'lie' will make him a bad boy, and I know he is not bad. How does this untruth come about?" "Well, we let him have the car since he is sixteen now, so he goes out at night and I stay up to kiss him good night. When I go in to kiss him, I ask him if he has been driving too fast, if he drank with the boys, or smoked with them. He answers 'no' to all these questions—and I know he does these things."

Then I said to her, "If your husband came home tonight and asked you if you had been out with the man next door, it would hurt you so bad to think he did not have any more confidence in you than that, you would not want to live with him. That is in reality what you are doing to your son. You have taught him that you doubt his living up to his training. He knows you would not ask him these questions if you had any confidence in him. He has nothing to live up to. If your husband told you that you were the poorest cook in town, you would not worry about making your meals beautiful and good, for there would be no incentive to try. You have one of the finest boys I know, and you are destroying him by making a nobody out of him. One day you two go out to lunch—just you two—and have a good talk about the younger generation. Tell him how disturbing it is to read and see so much about how many young people decide to follow the devil rather than God, but let him know just how much confidence you have in him.

"Tell him how important it is for a young man to think and decide for himself what he wants in life and make it clear that after a young man reaches sixteen, his parents can't make his decisions any longer. And say to him that you have been so anxious about him that you have shown him you did not have the confidence in him a mother should have in her son, but from now on you will not stay up until he comes in, and you will never ask him about his conduct for you know you can depend on him no matter where he may be."

I saw that mother several months later, and she said things had really changed. When her son found that she loved him enough to trust him, he could not help doing the right thing.

I have this story over and over again in my office. A mother and father with a teenage child will say to me, "We can't do anything with this child; we are helpless." That statement is really the truth. What can a mother and father do with a sixteen-year-old boy or girl? It is easy for them to say that as long as the child stays in their home, he must do what they say, but it will not work unless the parents have taught the child from birth to respect, honor, and obey. The job can't be started at sixteen. A boy or girl at this age cannot be made to do good; they must want to do the right thing.

There are four factors that make it easy for these young people to decide for good instead of evil. First, to have sixteen years of good training by parents who are an example of what they want their children to be.

Second, to teach them from birth to make decisions. For example, we should not say, "Don't touch that stove," but say, "If you touch that stove, you will get burned." "If you destroy your toy, you will want it one day, and we can't buy you another." Day in and day out we should teach our children to make decisions.

Third, we should make our children know that we have confidence in them. Lack of confidence has destroyed many wonderful people; for instance, parents who say, "He will not tell me the truth; he will not keep up with his school work; he will not go to school; he will not do anything I tell him to do; the boy next door is so perfect, but my son doesn't care about anything but to go spend money." An adolescent who hears these statements from parents or teachers has nothing to live up to, and he has nothing to lose; nobody has any confidence in him so it matters not what he does. If an adolescent knows that somebody really has confidence in him and expects him to make the right decisions, he will take time to think when a suggestion is made that will betray the confidence of this parent, teacher, preacher, girl friend, boy friend, good neighbor, or whoever the person may be.

I found that to be true in teaching. In my first school, I was teaching teenagers. When I arrived in that small town, the superintendent of the school said to me, "Miss Daughtry, you are going to teach some of the worst boys I have ever known." I was small in stature and just out of college, and I was to teach boys who were six feet tall and almost twice my size. At first thought I felt a little afraid. Then the thought came to me that I was once a high school girl and lived in the school with boys just as big as these. I was not afraid of them so why should I be afraid of these? I had been taught to do unto others as I would like them do unto me. So that first day I treated the boys and girls in my class like I would want a teacher to treat me, and I taught there nine months and never had the slightest bit of trouble.

I have found in the practice of medicine that if we say to a little boy or a big boy, "This is a fine boy and he always acts like a man," we have very little trouble. And as a mother, I know my child knew I had confidence in her and I never tried to make a nobody out of her. We should give our child a pat on the back and tell him how proud we are of him and what he means to us; always build him up and never run him down. It is difficult to betray the confidence of someone that you know really has confidence in you.

Fourth, in helping young people decide for good, let them know that we were once adolescents and we had every suggestion made to us that is made to our children and that we had to decide which road to take; that we had every feeling about our parents that our children have about us, and that there is nothing modern and there is nothing old-fashioned in the behavior of the human race.

Since the beginning of time, if boys or girls decide for evil we say they are modern; if they decide for good, we say they are old-fashioned. Evil is not modern and good is not old-fashioned, but they are two ways of life that have always been with us, and a boy or girl should learn the real meaning of these words.

It is sad to see how young people are deceived by the words "modern" and "old-fashioned." Take the word "modern" as it is used today in the behavior of a young person or any person: What does it suggest? The same thing it suggested as far back as history is recorded: simply, that a person who is modern lives as he likes and not as the laws of life say he must live; and a person that is "old-fashioned" lives as the laws of life say a person must live. Young people seem to get a great thrill from the word "modern" for it makes them feel that they are doing something new. They must know that there is not a sin on earth that is new and that any sin they commit has been committed over and over since the beginning of time, and the price to be paid for sin has not changed.

Young people want to explore, they want adventure, they want to excel, to go higher on the mountain, deeper in the cave, faster in the car, stay up later into the night, leave home, and make their own way. This drive they have is normal, yet they are led to believe that it is something new, something modern; and because their parents have passed through this stage and the drive is over, they are old-fashioned.

When parents come to me with these problems concerning young people, the first thing I have them do is to sit quietly for just one minute and try to recall their feelings when they were sixteen, how they felt about their parents and all adults, how the world seemed so slow and old-fashioned, how strict their parents seemed, how they had to be broken to harness. A good picture of an adolescent is a young colt. He can't be still; he kicks up his heels and gets hung in the fence. He is not doing this to get in trouble but he is just trying to see what he can do. That is so true of young people. They are trying to act like adults and they don't know how many mistakes these adults made before they learned how to live. One young boy said to me one day, "Oh, that I could be the man my father is." Then I said to him, "But your father was not the man he is today when he was your age. He made mistakes and had failures before he became the man he is today. As he tries to help you, he has to remember what his reaction was to the adult world when he was young and try to have patience with you and not make you feel that your actions are new or modern, or that you are different and a disappointment to your parents, and a nobody."

Once a young person finds out that the adults he knows do not expect anything good to come out of him, that adolescent is lost.

That something in a human being that makes him want to be recognized takes man to the highest peak of heaven or to the lowest pits of hades. The little colt did not need a psychiatrist to tell it why it kicked its foot into the fence; it was just trying to show the world what it could do and not be inhibited. Now the men and women these young people are trying to be like should be an example of what they want their children to be.

When children reach adolescence, they begin to judge their parents and find fault with the way they dress, act, and live. It is almost as common an occurrence to have these adolescents come to me with the parent problems as it is for the parents to come to me with the adolescent problems. This is the way it goes: "Doctor, Mother comes to school with tight pants on that she should not wear even at home, and I am so embarrassed." "Doctor, I wish you would talk to Mother and Daddy about their smoking. They tell me it is wrong, yet they are killing themselves, and mother's teeth are so dark and her skin so ugly. She could be a beautiful mother if she would do the right thing."

A girl came to me one day and this was her story: "Doctor, I went with my parents on vacation for the first time and I am heartbroken. I can't eat or sleep. I did not know they drank or smoked. Until this time I had thought they were perfect parents, and I can't get over what I learned." Another child said, "Doctor, my mother can't seem to get it into her head that I am not a baby; every time my friends are around she calls me all kinds of baby names and they laugh at me and call me a baby."

I would say that any young person would rather have parents that he could brag about than any other thing. Parents preaching without practicing has a great deal to do with our juvenile delinquent problems. The same is true of our teachers and preachers. We should not preach anything to these young people that we do not practice. It breaks my heart to have parents come to me with their adolescent problems and to hear how these young people, in whom they have put so much, decide for wrong and destroy the only life they will ever live . . . the only body they will ever have.

The saddest story on earth to me is the story an adolescent tells about parents who did not love enough to give a child a chance. I have young people come to me who almost hate themselves for feeling about their parents as they do because they have been taught that it is a sin not to honor one's parents. But how can they honor somebody who is not honorable? The parents tell the adolescent that it is wrong to drive too fast, smoke, drink, stay out all night, wear clothes that are too revealing, waste time, waste money, talk too loud, lose one's temper, and otherwise break the laws of life. Parents who do these things while telling their children not to do them make their children sin—if it is a sin to dishonor a parent that is not honorable. In such a case I believe the parent will have to take the punishment for the child's sin.

It is difficult to counsel a young person who says, "I am ashamed of my parents," when you know you would be ashamed of them if they were your parents. A big problem of adolescence is that at this age children want parents who are perfect, and parents want children who are perfect. It seems to me that if we could get these two persons—the parent and the child—to start with self and be sure they are each doing the right thing before they try to reform the other, we would go a long way toward solving this big problem.

One of the saddest pictures in this age group is the mentally retarded boy or girl who cannot keep up or compete with his or her age group. By this time parents should know just how much a child can do, but parents and teachers alike are not willing to accept the truth that a boy or girl just can't learn. They will accept the truth that a blind child can't see, a deaf child can't hear, but seem to think the dull child must keep up. And because he can't learn, he is called dumb or they say he doesn't try, or has his mind on something besides school, or is lazy. Out of this group come many of our juvenile delinquents. They are talked about, punished, and forced to try to do something they can't, so they become a nobody and it doesn't matter to them what they do since there is nobody who believes in them. They have been told so many times how worthless they are that they have to believe it is true, and they actually hate themselves. When most of the people in this country lived on the farm, boys or girls who reached adolescence and wanted to be adults but could not keep up in school could quit school and work on the farm. They did not have to go through all the abuse a mentally retarded boy or girl has to go through today.

Mothers bring these young people to me and say, "Doctor, this boy just will not study; he is not passing at all, and the teacher is after me all the time about the grades he is making. I help him all I can; we go over the work time and time again, and I think he will be able to keep up. But when he gets to school, he seems to forget all he knew. Things are bad, and I feel my child is doing all he can do. Should I take him out of that school and try another school? Do you think it is the teacher?" On and on these questions come. This is the child we hear the teachers talking about the first day of school. One will say, "Oh, you have Johnnie Doe this year. I am sure glad I did not get him. You will never be able to teach that boy anything." With that statement his new teacher starts off on a road of doubt and she looks for the worst in him . . . and he soon finds that out.

I tell these parents a change of school might help as this child has been put in a class of "no-goods" by the teachers and he knows it. In a new school, the teachers might try to help him since they do not know before they start that they are helpless to teach the child. After six years in school, we really know how much this child can learn and since he is forced to continue school until he is sixteen, we might try this method: treat him as we would treat a blind child. We should help all we can every day and never tell him he is lazy or that he is not doing his work because he is a bad boy, but we should say, "Son, I am willing to help you, and I know you are doing the best you can; all of us can't be at the top, but we must develop what we have and then if you don't pass your work, your mother and father will know you are doing your best; and if you can't learn as fast as some in your class, there are other things you can do well." Parents should make him know he has their love, and should respect him even though he can't compete, and keep telling him there is a place for him and that no matter how small the job is, if it is the best he can do, he is great. Teachers and parents have made a host of juvenile delinquents out of these mentally retarded people by making a nobody out of them.

In adolescence there is the birth of a true conscience and no matter how good or bad the past and the training have been, one still feels these two forces in himself that make adolescence a trying time in the human life. Parents who have done their best may be heartbroken over their adolescent's conduct, but it is impossible for the parents to make the decisions for their adolescent children. They may put them in all kinds of places where the influence is perfect, but each individual has to select his or her way of life. One may be born in the most undesirable home and yet come to the top if he decides on the side of right. Every child should have a good home and just parents to use as an example, but that is no assurance that he will follow their way of life any more than the unfortunate child will follow the way of his vulgar parents.

To sum it all up, from birth to two a child wants to be held, protected, and loved. From two to six, a child wants to do it himself, and finds out the things his parents stand for and learns a way of life. From six to adolescence, children are anxious to learn. They want a leader, they ask for and take advice, they believe and admire their parents and teachers, they like to help and be helped. Parents have complete control.

From adolescence on, parents find themselves unable to dominate as they have for the past twelve years. The adolescent feels a great urge to be free and run his own life; he has the desires of an adult, but the judgment of a child. The adolescent wants the perfect parents as much as the parents want the perfect child. This is the time when right and wrong seem to be in a furious battle over which force will dominate. It is a time when self-discipline is put into play to decide which will control the adolescent—right or wrong. It must be made plain to our adolescents that the laws of God will not let us put the blame on somebody else for our behavior. No matter how much we would like to blame our parents, teachers, school, or church for our acts, if we harm ourselves or our fellow man, we have to pay the price. No matter how much our parents would like to serve the sentence for us, that is not permitted by God or man.

At this period of life these young people should be taught that they can come to their parents and other adults for advice, but for them to develop into normal adults they must make the decisions as to their way of life. There is no parent who would not select for his son or daughter the most perfect way of life if he could make these decisions. Children must know that they have to make these decisions, and that there is something that dictates the right road if we will only follow through each day of our life with the best we can do, never missing an opportunity to learn all we can and to fit it into a pattern that will be the most rewarding to us and to our fellow man.

♂ ♀

3. Feeding children

The subject of feeding has been dealt with briefly in Chapter 1 since every mother wants the doctor at the first visit to discuss with her a proper feeding schedule for her newborn baby. In this chapter the subject is being dealt with in its broader aspects and, if comments contained in Chapter 1 are repeated here, it is being done only for emphasis.

In my youth a child was taken to a doctor for only one thing: he was sick with a fever. He had some disease—diphtheria, whooping cough, typhoid, diarrhoea, scarlet fever, pneumonia, or some other sickness. These illnesses took up all of the doctor's time. As a rule they were long-lasting and the doctor had no way to treat them except in a palliative way. There were no cures and the child had to build his own antibodies to cure himself; and the doctor tried to keep the child alive until he could cure himself.

Today these diseases do not worry a doctor as they did sixty years ago or so for the reason that we just don't have many of them any more. We have learned how to immunize against most of them and the others can be cured in a short time through use of our good drugs. I often say to my young mothers, "You should say a word of thanks each day for immunization and good drugs and for the blessing that your child does not have to suffer the long deadly illnesses your parents and grandparents had."

With all the work and dreams of doctors that one day we can keep people well and our work will be light, our offices are more crowded than ever.

It seems that the human race has lost its knowledge and wisdom about how to take care of the human body, what it should eat and drink, when it should eat and drink, how much it should eat and drink, and how the food and drinks should be prepared. So a large portion of the doctor's time is spent trying to teach people what to eat or drink, when to eat or drink and to patch up the bodies that have been damaged by dissipation and by improper feeding.

Breast Feeding

There is only one normal food to give a newborn baby and that is his own mother's milk nursed from the breast. In the past fifty years this method has fallen into disuse and is becoming obsolete but there can never be created an equal to this normal method even though it is worked out on the most scientific basis. The security, the antibodies, the mother-child relationship, the human protein cannot be created in a laboratory. These things count most in a child's life and cannot be obtained from any other source; so the breast milk makes the best method and is far superior to other foods in developing a child to his normal capacity.

We cannot make a mother nurse her baby any more than we can make a mother stay home and train that baby. So we come to the problem that is taking a great portion of the doctor's time and thoughts. The little babies that cannot be fed the way nature planned for them to be fed create a big problem. We can be assured that no two babies can be fed just the same way, so each baby is a new problem and must be worked out as a problem all his own. A mother will say, "Johnny took evaporated milk well, but Mary spits and has not gained on this milk." Each baby has to be tried on the formula the doctor and mother think is best and if the baby cries, spits, does not gain, develops a rash, is constipated or has too frequent stools, can't sleep, and shows other abnormal symptoms, there is something wrong with the baby or the food, and not a single one of these abnormal symptoms should be neglected, leaving the baby to suffer.

Many of these problems may lead to bigger physical and mental problems if neglected. Babies are not born bad, but something makes them bad, and the mother and the doctor should do everything in their power to give a baby a good start. No matter how well another baby—the mother's or neighbor's—did on a certain feeding, if the present baby develops abnormal symptoms on the formula, it should not be continued; instead this baby has a right to be worked up as a special problem and given a chance.

If a baby is on the breast and the mother does not take any laxatives, stimulants, narcotics, hypnotics, sedatives, alcohol, nicotine, or caffeine, she should be able to have a happy time with her baby for the first seven months. If the baby has become allergic to cow's milk by the mother's constant consumption of milk for nine months before the baby was born, the mother can leave off the milk in her diet while she nurses the baby and the spitting, crying, frequent stools, eczema, or other abnormal symptoms that are caused by the milk the baby is allergic to will disappear; and the mother can continue to nurse the baby. The mother of long ago did not know the word "allergy," but she knew that certain foods she ate and things she drank upset the baby so she left them off and did not take the baby off the breast.

Before a person can be allergic to a food or anything else, there must be some direct contact with that substance. I am of the opinion that if those women who are not planning to breast-feed their babies would not drink milk during pregnancy, they would not have a great deal of trouble getting the baby started on a cow's milk formula; and cow's milk seems to be our best and cheapest method of feeding these babies that the mother cannot or will not nurse. To leave off milk and milk products during her pregnancy would not be too much to ask a mother to do if she does not plan to nurse her baby.

The power to build up an allergic reaction to any substance differs with each individual. Some individuals seem to be able to develop an allergy to most any food or substance they come in contact with; others seem to be allergic to nothing and have no trouble. The woman who has a tendency to develop different kinds of allergies should be the one to take no milk during pregnancy if she is not going to nurse her baby . . . for her baby may have these allergic tendencies. If she is going to nurse her baby, it would not matter so much because she could leave off the milk if it seemed to disturb the baby.

Some doctors and medical books suggest milk to a mother who is nursing her baby as a way to make more milk and better milk. I have never been able to figure that out. If milk is such a good milk maker, why don't we feed it to the cow? She makes it, and she nurses her baby without drinking a drop herself. No other animal except man takes milk during the period of pregnancy or lactation to make milk for a finer baby, and all members of the animal kingdom seem to do a good job. In the past the Negro mothers on the farm were our best milk producers and they nursed their babies with perfect satisfaction, yet they were never a milk-drinking people.

The anemia of pregnancy is known to be greatest with white women and is not known in the pregnant cow as far as I can find out. The anemia of pregnancy continues to develop as the consumption of milk increases. Any animal consuming great quantities of milk after the sucking period develops anemia.

If the baby is on breast milk and develops symptoms of allergy and the offending foods are removed, the mother may tell her friends how well her baby did when she left off a certain food. When the second mother left off the same food, it is possible her baby did not improve. Mothers must know that what makes one baby sick may not hurt another. This is the reason why a certain food gets a bad name with nursing mothers. A nursing mother should eat her regular diet until symptoms appear, and then she should work out her problem by the process of elimination, leaving off the most common offenders one at a time. Chocolate would be first, milk next, tomatoes next—on and on she should go leaving off one food for two weeks. If there is no improvement, she should leave off another and go back on the food that did not seem to be the offender. This method has saved breast feeding many times.

It is quite common to have a mother bring in a baby that is having eczema, spitting, crying a great deal, and have her say, "Doctor, my milk seemed to upset the baby and I took him off the breast." Then we may find that this particular baby is allergic to cow's milk and the soybean feeding caused diarrhoea. It would have been much better if she had left off milk and kept the baby on the breast. These feeding problems are not hard to solve if we can get the mother to nurse the baby.

The mothers that breast-feed their babies often call and say, "My nurse tells me my breast milk is nothing but water." This is the reason why large numbers of babies are taken off the breast, the conclusion that the breast milk was either too weak or too rich. All milk looks the same the first few weeks of lactation. The milk has very little butter fat and that gives the bluish transparent color that is normal. The reason the baby cries is because there is not enough milk, or he is being fed too frequently, or he is allergic to something the mother is taking in the way of food or drink, or tobacco, or some drug. You could never make me believe that the human race is being cursed above all other animals and that the human mother is not able to furnish her young breast milk if she is willing to do her part.

We have become so scientific about pregnancy that it has become a sickness instead of a natural condition, and a woman is doctored during this period like a sick person. She has to take vitamins, calcium, iron, all kinds of shots, and must follow a special diet. Pregnancy is such a normal thing if only a woman will live and eat as a normal person. The animals seem to know what to eat and when to eat it. It sounds bad to say a woman does not have as much knowledge and judgment about her food as a cow. A woman should not go on a starvation diet when she is pregnant, but she should not be a glutton.

If a pregnant woman would eat a balanced diet, get the normal amount of sleep, continue to do her work, be happy in the prospect of becoming a mother, refrain from taking anything into her body that she would not want her baby to take, and not drink enough milk to make her anemic, she should in almost all cases be able to nurse her baby. With the periodic supervision of a good obstetrician to detect any complications that might occur, pregnancy should not cause any anxiety; and the mother-to-be should not go through that feeling, "I want to nurse my baby, but I am just sure I will not be able to do so."

A custom that has grown up in our crowded communities is very bad for all mothers, but worse for the pregnant women. The mother has a cup or two of coffee at breakfast with her husband, then at ten o'clock or so some friends drop in and they all have their morning coffee; at lunch she has coffee or tea, and in the afternoon a carbonated drink or coffee; then more coffee or tea for dinner. If one could add up the amount of caffeine thus consumed in a day, it would be more than six grains. Then when a pack or more of cigarettes is added to the caffeine, we would not expect the mother to be able to nurse her baby. She is a nervous wreck and must have a little phenobarbital or a tranquilizer to make her sleep at night. This is not fiction; I have been in this work a long time and I know from experience that this condition is becoming more prevalent all the time.

Formula Feedings

Without the mother's milk, a doctor must instruct the mother how to feed the baby so he will grow up to be as normal as possible. The first thing the doctor and mother must know is that the milk the baby should be getting is very low in butter fat and ash. The lower the fat, the better the appetite. The formula should simulate the human milk as nearly as possible. The high ash content in cow's milk acts as a buffer and neutralizes the hydrochloric acid in the stomach, causing a marked delay in the emptying of the stomach. So we must be sure that the feedings are spaced at least four hours apart if the child is to take cow's milk. Dr. Kim Merritt determined some fifty years ago that by the addition of enough lactic acid to form a curd and neutralize the buffer in cow's milk, the milk was made far more digestible. In 1928 we used lemon juice to form the curd and neutralize the buffer, which seemed even better as the curds were smaller and digestion was faster. The baby was started on half skimmed milk with an equal amount of water, enough acid to cause a curd, and enough carbohydrate added to make it simulate human milk. The amount of fat was gradually increased and the amount of water decreased until at seven months the baby was on whole milk and was taken off the bottle.

It is better to start a baby on a weak formula and gradually strengthen it as his digestive tract matures, which has to grow up just like the baby has to develop. A baby started on a strong formula may start spitting or having frequent fatty stools, may seem hungry and want to eat often since his stomach is hurting, or he may lose his appetite from nausea caused by the fat.

If a baby has been born normal and the mother can't nurse him, and he spits, cries, has frequent stools or is constipated, has eczema, or any other abnormal symptom, it will not help to give him atropine, phenobarbital, paregoric, laxatives, or any other kind of medicine. She should find out why the baby is having the trouble and eliminate the cause—not just cover it up. There is always a way to feed a baby, but it may take time and patience to determine the proper way. I always tell a mother if a food comes up, it should not have gone down. So first, we should eliminate any anatomical reason that might cause the trouble, such as sickness, and should help the mother to develop the proper psychological attitude. With these situations corrected, we know the food must be the cause of the trouble.

The market is flooded with all kinds of milk preparations and milk substitutes, but no one food is the answer for all babies. It takes an interested doctor and a patient mother to work these problems out, and if the doctor will listen to the mother, she can be a great help. She sees the stools and the milk that comes up, and the type of stool and the type of milk that comes back may help a great deal in planning the formula.

First, the formula should be made weak in butter fat, and undiluted milk should never be used to start with. The milk should be warm. There is a fad today of giving newborn babies cold milk right out of the icebox. We know that by cooling we decrease metabolism and, if a baby is given cold milk, the process is slowed up; therefore, we must try our best to simulate human milk that is always given warm. We adults know how a warm glass of water, milk, or soup relaxes the body, and if we want to keep the newborn baby relaxed as much as possible, we should never offer him a bottle of cold milk.

The baby should have as much as he will take in twenty minutes. There should be a cross cut in the nipple so the milk comes freely, but will not come when the baby is not sucking. The feedings should be four hours apart as long as the baby is on milk alone; then when a large amount of solid food is added, the feedings should be five and one-half hours apart. No matter how little or how much the baby takes, the spacing should be maintained.

All newborn babies associate pain with hunger and if they have a pain of any kind, they want to suck, thinking that will give them relief. This problem causes more trouble with newborns than any one other thing. When a baby cries and gnaws his hands, the statement is frequently made, "That baby is just hungry and he should be fed." There are thousands of reasons why a baby would cry but feeding seems to be the only one that the average person can think of. Adding more food to the stomach that has not had time to empty makes the condition worse. When the family gets all tired out and gives up, the baby gets better.

Demand feedings have been the talk for a short time. About forty years ago a move was started never to inhibit a child for fear he would develop a complex. The advocates of this philosophy argued that the lower animals were not inhibited and they were a happy lot. I am sure that the person who started the story about the lower animals not being inhibited never lived on a farm or observed animals closely. This word "inhibit" may be called instinct in the lower animals but the animal has a definite way of life and does not vary. Animals have a time to eat. Hogs in a peanut patch will eat for awhile, then they will go get a drink of water and find a mudhole and sleep until the food is digested. No matter how much you wake them up, they will not go back to eating until their stomachs are empty. The same is true of all animals. A bird feeds her young at the same time each day. We need not go fishing just any time of the day and expect the fish to bite, for they have a certain time to feed.

The digestive system is made up a certain way, and we can't change our anatomy. The stomach retains food in the same place longer than at any other step in the entire tract; and it must have time to digest the proteins before they leave the stomach. A baby that is fed too often develops a pot belly; and if his stomach is X-rayed, it will be found to be much larger than it should be just because it never has a chance to empty one meal before another is added.

So the fad of not inhibiting a child has been carried into his eating habits and has caused the mother and father to completely neglect their home and themselves. Every time the baby cries they are told by advocates of demand feeding to run for the bottle so that is all they have time to do. The baby's distended stomach causes colic all the time, so the baby is a constant care. In fact, caring for the baby is all they have time to do: no meals for them together, no system of getting papa off to work to an office where the boss doesn't believe in coming to work on demand.

So the family really gets frustrated with the mother-father relationship wrecked as well as the baby. The parents must have a system for getting their food and doing the work they must do to make a normal home for their baby.

This is a picture I get in my office every day. Here come mama and papa both looking tired and worn out; mama has a two weeks' old baby in a blanket (usually too much blanket). They are called in and asked what their trouble is. Papa usually speaks up first, "Doctor, this baby has not let us have a night's sleep since we got him home; he cries all the time." Then mama speaks up, "And he takes only about one ounce of milk at a time and he spits that up, but he continues to cry like he is hungry." Then the question, "How old is this baby?" "Two weeks." "Was it a normal birth?" "Yes." "Did you take alcohol, tobacco, coffee, sedatives, or other drugs while you were pregnant?" "No."

"Does he sleep on his back?" "Yes." "How would you like to have somebody put you down on your back and leave you if you were as helpless as this little baby? He has been held tight for nine months; now you put him on his back, and when his arm or leg drops, he thinks he is falling and it scares him to death. With the sudden fear of falling, the baby cries out and swallows air that gives him the colic . . . then he cries from the colic . . . and swallows more air. Every baby swallows air when he is frightened, when he takes his bottle, and when he cries for the first three months of life. How would you like to have colic flat on your back? You would think you were going to die. If spitting up, he might strangle. He passes off the air he has swallowed better when he is on his abdomen and his heart beats more normally in this position.

"Everything works right on the abdomen and nothing works right on the back. So let's put him on his abdomen all the time except when he is eating, at which time you should hold him tight like he was nursing the breast.

"Do you put oil or anything else on his skin?" "Yes." "How would you like to have a nice clean bath and then have somebody cover you with oil? A baby can't feel warm if his body is covered with oil. If you perspire under oil, it cannot evaporate so it is like wearing wet clothes all the time. It causes the baby to get chilled and that lowers the white cell count in his blood and he will develop a cold. Let's wash him clean with soap and water and put a little powder on his buttocks, if it is necessary for an irritation."

The next question, "What is your formula?" "We are making the formula of one can evaporated milk, one can water, three table-spoons Karo." "A little baby's intestinal tract and his digestive power are immature and have to mature along with the rest of his body. So, at birth he cannot digest food like he can at six or eight months of age, and the formula must simulate human milk. Human milk is low in calcium and phosphorus.

"Cow's milk has ten times as much calcium and phosphorus as human milk and the baby is not developed enough to utilize this large amount of ash. So, if the baby is fed that type formula, he may spit up or have diarrhoea, or constipation, or colic, and in a very short time you will find that the growing areas of the bones are much enlarged. The wrists, ankles, and ends of ribs become en-larged, the head takes on an angular appearance, and the baby de-velops anemia due to the marked increase of bony formation in the medullary cavity of the long bones. A formula made as you are mak-ing this one would be too high in butter fat. A newborn cannot digest that much fat. With a formula of that type, the proteins are too high. The baby is not able to eliminate the by-products of that much protein and the baby can become ill.

"If you are to use evaporated milk, it is best to start with one part milk, two parts water, and enough carbohydrates to bring the sugar up to the equivalent of human milk. A good starter would be six ounces evaporated milk, twelve ounces water, and two tablespoons dextro-maltose. Give three ounces at six, ten, two, six, and ten o'clock. If the baby takes all of the three ounces, next time make up enough to put four ounces in each bottle in the same proportion until the baby eventually gets eight ounces at six, ten, two, and six o'clock. The formula will be assimilated much better if you add one teaspoon of lemon juice to each eight ounces of formula, or twelve drops of lactic acid to each eight ounces or enough to make a curd—after the formula is cold. The same formula could be made from fresh cow's milk using two parts milk, one part water, and, for the first three months, taking off half the cream. Boil the milk and water five minutes in a covered boiler and when cold, add the lemon juice or lactic acid and the sugar. The milk should form a fine curd and separate.

"There are many good powdered milks that work well. From some of them the ash has been removed to simulate human milk and the animal fat has been replaced with vegetable fat. If these milks are diluted right and given in a diluted form to start with, they are well tolerated if the baby is not allergic to milk or the sugar that is added. At six weeks the average baby will be taking eight ounces at six, ten, two and six o'clock.

"Always cut a cross in the nipple one sixteenth inch both ways, being sure it is cut the same on both sides in and out. This can be done well with a number eleven Bard-Parker knife. Then, when the baby mashes down on the nipple, the cross opens up and he gets a swallow of formula. When he takes a breath, the cross closes up and cuts the formula off so he will not strangle. Now if you burn a hole in a nipple, the formula continues to flow and the baby can't take a breath without getting strangled. The milk should be the same temperature as human milk. If the baby refuses the bottle and there is no evidence of sickness, and the formula is without fault, don't force the baby. If the baby takes all the bottle, increase the amount when you make the next formula.

"We cannot predetermine a fixed amount for a baby, as the metabolism in every baby is different. We should dilute the milk properly, and then let the baby take what he wants in twenty minutes. A strong, happy baby will take all he wants in a much shorter time; seven minutes is not too fast. On the breast the average baby gets all there is in one breast in about seven minutes. Nursing too long on the bottle injures the epithelium on the tongue and the mouth. If you look at the tongue of a baby that is allowed to nurse a nipple of any kind for a long time, you will see that the taste buds are flat and the tongue is red and more susceptible to thrush. Also, I am sure the tongue burns and the taste is not normal. Nature made the human breast nipples the softest part of the body. The covering over the nipple is like velvet and we have never been able to make a nipple that could simulate the normal human nipples; therefore, we should not let a baby suck on a rubber nipple for a long time and injure his tongue. It takes effort to nurse and if a baby is allowed to nurse for a long time, he gets tired. The longer the baby nurses, the more air he swallows, and the more air he swallows, the more colic he has. He swallows air through his nose every time he sucks and soon he is so distended he will bring the air up and also the formula or cry from the colic.

"Your attitude towards this baby means a great deal as to the way he eats and the amount he eats. If you try to force him, he will soon hate the bottle and every feeding time will be a time to cry. It is not uncommon for a mother to say, 'Doctor, this baby cries every time he is fed.' I can't think of anything that would be worse for your baby than to be unhappy at eating time, as he can't digest his food when he is unhappy.

"When you bring the bottle in, you should be happy and not in a hurry. Handle the baby as though you have no doubt that he will take the bottle and like it. I have mothers come in and say, 'I can't get my baby to take his bottle.' The first two words in that statement should never be used before your child no matter how small or how weak he is. The words, 'I can't,' have ruined thousands of children when said by their superiors. Don't approach the baby with a defeated look, for you can't fool a baby. Just give him what he will take and be happy about it. Make him think it is a privilege to get food and not a task. Now if the food is unpleasant or makes the baby sick, he will refuse it, and a mother can soon learn if it is the food or her defeatist attitude that makes him refuse it. Mealtime should be the happiest time of the day.

"After the baby is fed, you should hold him up in front of you with his back to your abdomen, in a standing position with his head straight up, holding his hands with one hand, and placing the other hand over his abdomen. Press a little on his abdomen and he will bring up the air he has swallowed while nursing. Then place him on his abdomen." Then the mother will say, "When I put him on his abdomen, he brings up all his food." My reply is, "If he has to be on his back to keep his food down, you are giving him the wrong food; and if he spits up on his back, he has no way to turn over and he might strangle to death or get milk in his lungs causing pneumonia. On his abdomen the food goes out on the bed and no harm is done but to a sheet."

The mother asks, "What about vitamins?" I say, "I would keep the baby out in the open as much as possible and, when the sun is out, I would give him a sun bath, just sunning his back a few minutes each day. Then you could give him one of the many vitamins in a small amount with the ten o'clock morning feeding." "What about orange juice?" "That is not necessary if there is lemon juice in the milk or if the baby is taking a vitamin that contains vitamin C. Breast-fed babies need no extra vitamins." "What about prune juice?" "If the formula is right, the baby will not need that." "What about water?" "Water should be offered twice a day for the first two or three months and dextrose should be added to change the surface tension so the baby will not strangle. But the baby really gets all the water he needs in his formula and offering water between feedings just makes extra work for the mother and may cause the baby to take less formula or breast."

"The baby should be kept on his abdomen all the time and should be carried on the arm with his face down and to the side. He should be held close to your body to make him feel secure." The mother will say, "Doctor, we have one of those seat baby carriers. What do you think of that?" "To me the use of one of those boards gives the impression of a rejected child. A baby likes to be cuddled and held tight. The warmth of the parent's body is soothing and acts like a sedative to a child's body, and no child should be deprived of this wonderful feeling of security. On this board the baby has to be on his back and that gives him a very insecure feeling."

After a talk with these new parents, they go out to try to make a go of the most rewarding job on earth, developing a baby. If they have a system, they will have time for each other and will have a happy baby.

At the conclusion of this first visit they ask, "When shall we come back?" "When the baby is three months old; until then if you need me, call." Most of the time I don't see them until the baby is three

months old. At three months the mother and father return with the
baby. It is always good for the father to come for with him present
there is a better understanding as to what to do. My first question,
"How is the baby today?" "Doctor, I tell you that good system saved
our home. The day we came in here we were just about ready to
give this job up as hopeless. We have no complaints. He is the best
baby in the world and we have time for each other and for our
friends."

This story might not have been this perfect if the baby had been
allergic to cow's milk. In that case we would have tried goat's milk
and if that did not work, we would have tried one of the soy bean
preparations. If that did not work, meat base formula would have
been tried. If the baby continued to cry, spit, have abnormal stools,
rash—and if no other reason could be found to cause the trouble
except the food—then I would try the "witch's brew," prepared as
follows: one cup brown rice, two quarts water, cook two hours, rub
through sieve, add enough water to make two quarts, one teaspoon
salt, four tablespoons dextrose, four tablespoons Knox Gelatine, boil
three minutes, and give as much as the baby will take at six, ten,
two, six and ten. This has saved many babies. We always make up
two quarts as it can be kept safely for two to three days; and it is
some trouble to prepare.

If the mother had smoked for nine months before the baby was
born, changing formulas would not have improved his condition.
Only time and vitamin B complex with vitamin C given intra-mus-
cular seem to help these little unfortunate babies. It takes about four
months to get them off the tobacco and get them relaxed and able
to keep their food. Many babies of this type are taken from doctor
to doctor and given all kinds of antispasmodics and sedatives and
formula changes, but it takes time for them to adjust their bodies to
a life without tobacco. This is true in cases where the mother took
drugs of any kind. It is so important to get a good history on the
mother when a baby is brought in with a feeding problem, as it may
not be food that is causing the trouble. If a baby does not eat and
develop normally, there is a reason and that reason should not be
covered up by giving the baby drugs to keep him quiet.

Feeding the Three Month Old Baby

At three months the baby is examined and a new schedule worked
out. The baby has gained one ounce a day since his last visit and has

started talking back to you in a little babble, smiling when you smile. He has grown four inches. The amount of milk he takes is now eight ounces at six, ten, two and six, and he sleeps all night. He has one or two formed stools each day. He holds his head up, and the body is firm and pink in color. The baby is happy, moves over the bed, follows light, recognizes the different members of the family, and laughs out loud. At this visit, solid food is started, with one new food each week to ascertain if he is allergic to these new foods. Cereal is started first with one-fourth teaspoon at ten, two, and six, increased each day until two tablespoons are given at ten, two and six.

The second week fresh banana is started in the same way and increased to two tablespoons at ten, two, and six. (The bananas should always be washed in Clorox water as soon as they are brought in from the market and, if possible, they should be bought with a portion of the stalk so the ends of the bananas cannot become contaminated.) The third week apple sauce or prunes will be started in the same way and increased to two tablespoons at ten, two, and six. (If the stools are hard, prunes will be started; if the stools are too soft, apple sauce is started.)

The fourth week beef or liver is started in the same way and increased to two tablespoons at ten, two, and six. The fifth week green beans or carrots are started in the same way and increased to two tablespoons at ten, two, and six. All of this is mixed well in a stainless steel or Pyrex boiler and enough of the formula added to make the food the right consistency. The consistency varies with the baby as some babies like the food rather stiff and others like it soft. Then all the food is cooked together while stirring for three minutes, cooled, and fed to the baby before the bottle is given. If the food is prepared in this manner, one can be sure it is sterile.

All of these foods should be mixed together and made to taste as much like chewed food as possible. Mothers chewed for their babies until they were able to chew for themselves before Louis Pasteur told mothers about germs. When a mother chewed for her baby, the food tasted sweet as the bread in the morsel she chewed with the other food changed into sugar in the mouth, making the morsel sweet, and babies like food that has a sweet taste. By mixing all the food, the baby cannot just take the sweet fruit and leave off the meat and vegetables. The food all tastes good.

At the three-month visit, the mother is advised to put the baby on a pallet on the floor so he can have more freedom of movement and learn to crawl, a thing that is so important in the development of the body. She is advised to keep the baby out in the open as much as possible and to talk to the baby in clear well-formed words.

The nap should be continued from ten in the morning to two in the afternoon, with no other planned naps, and a strict schedule should be maintained if the mother wants a secure baby. No baby can feel secure unless he knows what to expect, and keeping a good schedule from the day a baby is born is the way security is taught. A mother with a plan builds a baby with a life that he knows how to use. This early advice to a young mother may save her home. At the end of the three-month visit, the mother is advised to return when the baby is five months old.

The Baby at Five Months

When the baby is five months old, he is brought back. The baby is fat, happy, laughing out loud, handling his toys well, can almost sit alone, can make his way over the floor, but cannot crawl on his hands and knees very well. He has gained three-fourths of an ounce a day since his last visit and is two inches longer.

At this visit he is put on three meals a day and three bottles given at seven, twelve-thirty, and six. At breakfast he gets one egg yellow, three tablespoons cereal, small amount of meat, banana, prunes or apple sauce; all the food mixed together as before. At this time he is given at the end of the meal a small amount of crisp bacon (the white only), and a small piece of toast. This is to teach him how to handle dry food. He holds this bacon and toast in his hand and feeds himself. At the end of the meal, an eight-ounce bottle of formula is given.

Each new food is added in the same manner as at three months to ascertain if he is allergic to any food. If he is allergic we will discover it as we add foods. At the twelve-thirty lunch he is given two tablespoons of meat, three tablespoons vegetables, two tablespoons cereal or potato, two tablespoons cooked fruit, one banana and eight ounces of milk. All of the food should be mixed and heated three minutes to be sure it is sterile, and then fed to the baby with the spoon with which it was stirred while heating, and fed out of the container in which it was heated. This makes less work for the mother and we can be sure the food is not contaminated. Some babies will not eat this much and many babies will eat more.

The amount a baby will take varies and if he wants more, more should be mixed in the same proportion, or less if he wants less. There can be no set amount as metabolism will vary. One thing to remember is that the food should always be mixed in the right proportion, and the baby should be the one to decide how much he wants. An effort should be made to get the baby to eat, but he should never be forced and made to cry and be unhappy about what he has to eat. Eating must be a happy time if the baby is to be normal.

The six o'clock afternoon meal is prepared in the same proportions as the lunch or twelve-thirty meal. Meat, cereal or potato, vegetables, cooked fruit and raw fruit (apple or banana), eight ounces of formula. At the five-month check-up the baby is given the first diphtheria-whooping cough-tetanus vaccine and the first polio vaccine. At this visit the baby is measured and checked. The urine is checked and a hemoglobin (red, white, and differential) is done, and the stools are examined.

After the examination is finished and a written outline is given to the mother, the question comes, "When shall we bring the baby back?" "At his six-month birthday." At that time he is not examined unless the mother thinks he is not doing well. He is given the second diphtheria-whooping cough-tetanus vaccine and the second polio vaccine. "When shall we come again?" "At his seven-month birthday." At this visit the baby is examined and measured. He can say "dada," can crawl, and can sit alone. He has gained one-half ounce a day since his last visit. The diet remains the same. He is given the third diphtheria-whooping cough-tetanus vaccine and the third polio vaccine.

Eight Months

At eight-months he is back again. At this visit he can pat-a-cake, say "bye-bye" and "dada," pulls up on his knees, weighs about ten pounds more than he did at birth, his head and chest measure about the same—around seventeen inches—he is about twenty-nine inches long, not fat but firm, and, as a rule, he has six teeth. The blood and urine are checked this time. At this visit the mother is advised to take the baby off the breast if he is a breast-fed baby, or off the bottle

if a bottle baby. The amount of milk consumed is cut to four ounces
with each meal and, if the hemoglobin is below seventy, no milk at
all is given. She is advised to start feeding the baby small portions of
food that she prepares for the family, but to be sure to mash it well
and continue to mix the food. The baby can have beans, squash,
beets, cabbage (and other members of the cabbage family if cooked
only ten minutes), blackeyed peas, green peas, tomatoes; but no
nuts, raw peaches, berries, melons, corn, new potatoes, or bought
ice cream. The formula is stopped, and pasteurized milk is given, but
it should be warmed. The mother is advised as to the value of warm
food, that cold food slows up the digestive process, and the soothing
effect of warm food is important. She is reminded that feeding between meals will cause a delayed emptying of the stomach and the
baby, if fed between meals or closer than five and one-half hours,
will become pot-bellied, be a feeding problem, and perhaps develop
anemia. One cannot stress too much the value of a good feeding
schedule and a well-balanced diet if one wants to give a child a
chance.

Then the question about juice comes up. When and how much
should a child have? Really, a child doesn't need anything to drink
except water. All kinds of drinks are on the market to buy, but a child
doesn't need that extra sugar. If given between meals, the drinks
cause a feeding problem, and the money spent on them should be
put on good food. As to carbonated drinks, the mother should be
advised very early about this. Carbonated drinks etch the teeth, causing decay and no child should have such drinks at all. There are too
many things sold today that will destroy little children, while making
somebody rich. There should always be a cup of water on the table
for the baby, and no food or drink should be given between meals
except water. The meals should be at seven, twelve-thirty, and six.
The baby should be fed sitting up in a chair before the family eats,
and the baby can nibble on a piece of toast while the family eats.

At the eight-month visit the baby is schicked and an agglutination
test made for whooping cough immunization. I have been making
this agglutination test since 1936. If the schick is negative and the
agglutination test four-plus, I never give booster shots of diphtheria-
whooping cough-tetanus vaccine. These tests have saved the children many, many shots and the parents money, and I have never had
a case of whooping cough if we gave enough of the vaccine to get a

four-plus agglutination. With this test the mother can be sure her child is immune to whooping cough.

At this visit the baby gets the first typhoid vaccine. One week later he gets the second typhoid vaccine, and one week later the third typhoid vaccine and the smallpox vaccination. The vaccination is always covered with a sterile gauze dressing that is not disturbed or made wet for twenty-eight days. The mother is advised that the baby will run a fever for three days starting one week after the vaccination and that aspirin is all the medication needed.

At nine months the baby gets the measles inoculation. At ten months the baby is examined, blood and urine checked as well as weight, length, head, chest and stool. By this time he is eating well from the table.

At one year he is checked and at that time he is walking, talking and feeding himself with some help. His weight is about twenty-two pounds, his height thirty inches, his head nineteen inches, and his chest nineteen inches. He has his stools on a training chair and the diapers are left off. There is no force used in toilet training. He should be helped but never punished if he has a mishap and should be told what a big boy he is if he goes to the toilet. His nap is from 10:00 A.M. to 12:00 noon with no afternoon naps and he goes to bed immediately after he has his supper. His meals are always spaced five and one-half hours apart, with no food or drink between meals except water.

I will not see him again until he is eighteen months old. Mama and papa come again and they are very happy with this fine baby. He is a big boy, talking, walking well by himself, plays with his toys, can climb on top of the tables, can open and close doors. He is at an age when he must be watched more than at any other time for he has very little judgment about what he eats or drinks, hot stoves, or high places. His body is fat, but he has gained only two pounds in six months and one and one-half inches in height; he has sixteen teeth. The feedings are the same as at one year. At this visit the parents are advised to come back when the baby is two years old.

From Two to Six: The Importance of a Good Schedule

At the second birth date mama and papa return with little Johnny. "Well, how is that fine boy today?" "Well, doctor, I don't know.

Something has happened to him. Maybe we just don't know how to
handle him, or we have done something wrong. He has completely
changed. Every time we tell him to do something or to eat his food,
he says, 'No,' and he sticks to it, We have tried talking to him, we
have tried letting him get a prize, and we have tried spanking also.
We have tried making him do without something he really wants,
like the dessert, and nothing works. He will not eat enough to keep
a bird alive. Look at his legs. Those beautiful little chubby legs are
just getting skinny. He will drink a little milk and that is about all
the food he gets. No matter how attractive I fix the food, he refuses
it. I have tried playing games with him to get a little food down and
I have threatened to give his food to his dog. Papa will try racing
with him at the table, but he will just sit there and play in his food
and not put one bit in his mouth. He has temper tantrums when he
can't have his way, and he whines and cries at the least interference
with his desires. We are really desperate; he has been a perfect child
for two years and now it seems we have struck a stone wall. Do you
think we should go to a psychiatrist? The trouble must be with us."

"Your problem is not so big if you only understand a two-year-old
child. From birth to two, if a child is fed right and trained right and
has a good schedule, he is very dependent on his parents. He eats
well and likes to do things to make his parents happy, and will do all
kinds of tricks to get his parents and their friends to laugh. If you
ask him to sing for daddy, he will sing and if you ask him to do some
stunts for his mama, he will do that. He will eat what you prepare
for him and sometimes ask for more. Up to two years your child was
as perfect as a little boy could be. He ate more the first two years
than he will eat for the next four. Johnny is a fine boy and a very
normal boy. He can't be a baby always and now that his baby days
are over, he is growing up.

"All children, if they are normal, begin to live a negative life when
they get to be two years old. This period of conduct will last until
he is six years old. If you say, 'Johnny, eat your breakfast', he will say,
'No.' If you say, 'Johnny, you can't have your breakfast,' he will kick
and scream until he gets it. If you say, 'You can't have your dessert
until you eat your meat,' he will sit there and show you he is not a
monkey on a string. No, he is not a baby any longer and from here
on out he will run his life. He gets down on the floor and bumps his
head until he gets his way. He whines all the time, and has given up
his good toilet habits."

This is the period in a child's life that is blamed on a new baby, as it is often the case that about the time a child turns two, there is a new baby in the house. I hear this statement over and over, "My child was perfect until the new baby arrived; being jealous of the new baby has completely changed his life." No, the new baby in a home is not the reason why a two year old changes. The new baby could be a contributing cause for trouble as the mother starts saying, "Don't bite the baby; don't touch the top of his head; don't throw toys in the baby's bed; don't cry and wake the baby up; don't wet your pants and make work for me when I am trying to care for the baby; go out and play so I can look after your little brother; hurry up and eat for I must feed the baby." Now all these suggestions give the two year old a chance to cause trouble because he will react with a strong negative response to any suggestion, baby or no baby. The mother should not make all these suggestions if she does not want the problem. Many times a mother creates a real hate for the new baby by the two year old in her constant nagging, because he is at a stage in his life when he will fight back no matter how big the commander is. We should never suggest evil to our children, and we could save them a lot of punishment. Neither the new baby in the home nor any other excuse we have when we see our perfect baby give up his perfect way of life is the reason, and we must know that these excuses we use are issues that have been suggested to the two year old that he can use to show he is not a baby any more. The greater the nagging, the greater the problem.

"Now what can be done about this problem? The first time you came into my office you were in just as bad a state; you were ready to give up. That worked out and this will also if you understand your problem. You have been good parents and have made this little boy a good body, so we must not fail at this point.

"The first thing I want you to do is to write a little sign and paste it across your bedroom mirror letting it read this way, 'I will never do or say anything to this little boy I would not want done or said to me.' As I have said, he is living a negative life and that will last four years. He will rebel to show you he is not about to be a baby any longer and nothing you have done makes him this way. This behavior pattern is just as normal as cutting teeth, but there is much that you can do to make this stage in his life his downfall.

"First, never give him a command that you can't carry through. Never give him a command in a manner you would not want to be

commanded. It is just as easy to say, 'Sweetheart, here is your breakfast,' as it is to say, 'Here is your breakfast—eat it.' It is just as easy to
say, 'Son, when you have to urinate, if you would go to the bathroom, your legs would not be all wet and cold,' as to say, 'If you wet
your pants, you are going to get a spanking.' Watch your words; if
you give a direct command, he may respond with a direct 'No' and
you must be big enough to see that he does what you command,

"There are three very important things in our lives we have to do
and these three play a great part in the negative period of a child's
life. They are eating, sleeping, and eliminating. A child soon learns
that his parents can't make him do any one of these vital things. You
can put him to bed, but you can't make him go to sleep; you can
take him to the bathroom, but you cannot make him have a stool or
urinate; you can take him to the table, but you cannot make him eat,
or, if you do, he can vomit. So these are the greatest problems at this
age. Never make any one of these things an issue, for if you give a
direct command about one of these things, he can show you you are
not adequate or big enough to handle him.

"Never say before him that you can't make him drink his milk,
you can't make him eat his food, you can't make him stop whining,
you can't make him go to the bathroom, for as you say these things
before him, his chest gets bigger and bigger. He knows that he has
grown up and now his parents are his subjects. From the cradle to
the grave we like people who are strong enough to stand up for
what is right, and we have no respect for a weakling. Your son is no
exception. When a child finds that his parents are not big and strong
enough to guide, he becomes disturbed and insecure.

"Now as to the eating. When a child reaches two years, his growth
almost stops. He has gained thirty pounds in the past two years and
nine months and will gain only three pounds in the next twelve
months. He has grown thirty-two inches in the past two years and
nine months and will grow only three inches in the next twelve
months and maybe not that much. He does not need to consume
more than one-fifth as much food as he did at the time he was one
year old. So you see he is not really hungry and it is not hard for him
to hold out when you try to force him. The things we have to do
become work; the things we want to do become play; and eating
should not be work.

"Food should be served on the child's plate in small portions,
never discussing his likes and dislikes before him, but if you know a

food is unappetizing to him, just don't put it on his plate; you would not want it on yours. After the plate is served, return thanks and then talk about anything except his food. When you and your husband have finished the meal, clear the table and never say, 'Johnny, why did you not eat your meat or drink your milk? That will make you big like Daddy.' Just be happy about the whole thing and never mention the food, no matter how little he ate, and give him no food or drinks except water until the next meal. If you find that he is eating no food off his plate except his potatoes, don't make an issue of that; just stop cooking potatoes for a while. If he just drinks milk, stop the milk for a while but don't say to him, 'I am going to stop the milk if you don't eat your food.' That provides him a challenge and nothing is quite so great as a challenge to a two year old. He will tackle any challenge and he goes in to win but if you make a threat, you must be strong enough to carry it through or you destroy your child's respect for you. From two to six a child is braver than he will ever be again for he will defy a papa that weighs two hundred pounds. He must have a balanced diet, and he will get that if you leave off the things he should not have and never let him eat or drink between meals. Once you say, 'You can't have your dessert unless you eat what is on your plate,' be sure to carry through.

"This little boy from two to six will learn all the discipline and the value of discipline he will ever learn. That is why he should live with his parents at this all-important period in his life. He will not act without an audience and his parents make the only audience that matters. If he is sent to a nursery school or kindergarten, he will not rebel for he does not have the proper audience. This business of rebellion and learning what it gets him is a lesson that cannot be missed. This period in a child's life determines whether he will be man or mouse. So don't worry about the amount of food he eats but about the type and quality of food he gets. Every day I hear parents say, 'Doctor, I would give him anything he might ask for just to get something in him.' Eating time should be the happiest time of the day and it can be if the parents will not nag any more than they would like to be nagged."

I am sure this period in a child's life causes more concern than any other period and the doctor is visited to get a tonic, vitamins, iron pills . . . something to get Johnny to eat or make him gain weight. A great number of these children really get in bad health. They get anemic, pot-bellied, sometimes emaciated, and many of them get slick tongues and evidence of pellagra in a land of plenty. Vitamins and iron are not the answer. Some of these children are put in hospitals, are tranfused for their anemia, are force fed, are sent to family service; and the parents continue to go from doctor to doctor trying to find the answer. It is simple and easy if there are parents who really love the child.

This is the way the story goes very often in my office. Mrs. Smith brings in Martha, age three. She is thin, pale, her tongue is slick, she has no energy, cries easily, and has a very dejected look. I ask the mother what the trouble is and she will say, "Doctor, she just won't eat a thing. I have tried to feed her, I have tried all kinds of vitamins and iron, and I have taken her to a number of different doctors. It won't do a bit of good to give her medicine." I get a history on the child. She was fine for the first two years, "fat as a little pig," she had measles, mumps or something else, or they had to move and Martha had to leave her friends, or her father drinks, or her grandparents were the beginning of the trouble. So many times the excuse for behavior is a new baby in the home. There is always an excuse and the blame put on something or somebody.

Then I ask the question, "What time does this little girl get up in the morning?" "Well, I just let her sleep in the mornings until she wants to get up—I would say about nine or ten o'clock or later." "What will she eat for breakfast?" Then the answer is, "Nothing." "Well, what do you fix?" "Anything she will suggest. Maybe some dry cereal or a glass of milk but she just sits there and maybe she will take one or two bites." "When will she eat again?" "Oh, about twelve-thirty." "Will she have anything between the two meals?" "If she wants it, she usually eats some cookies and has a bottle drink or a glass of milk." "What will she eat at the noon meal?" "Nothing." "What will you fix?" "Maybe some soup or a sandwich but she never eats much of that." "When will she eat again?" "About five P.M. Her father gets home at that time and he likes to eat early as he has very little lunch." "Does she eat an afternoon snack?" "Yes, usually a little juice and cookies or milk; she likes to take the bottle." "How about supper?" "Oh, I fix a good supper; my husband is a big eater and I have meat, vegetables, a starch, and a dessert." "What will she eat at that time?" "She will drink her milk and eat the dessert." "Then does she go to bed?" "Oh, that girl will not go to bed until we do, about eleven o'clock." "Does she eat after supper?" "Yes, we always keep drinks and cookies and plenty of milk so when she asks for some-

thing, we can get it for her. I feel that if I can get something in her—
no matter what it is—it is better than nothing."

The child is examined. She may be very thin or she may appear fat
as she has a large abdomen. Her hair is dry, skin dry and rough, her
body has the feel of an old person, her teeth have many cavities and
the enamel on her teeth is so etched that the teeth look like chalk
and there may be several gumboils. Her tonsils may be large from
constant sucking and frequent infections of the throat. All cervical
glands may be enlarged and sometimes there is a general enlarge-
ment of all the lymph glands in a child like this. The urine is alkaline
and most of the time there is a trace of sugar and a few pus cells.
Her hemoglobin is fifty per cent. She has a high lymphocytes count;
the red cells look thin, pale, and fragile. The blood count sometimes
makes me fear that this may be a lymphatic leukemia. She has a slight
systolic murmur.

After the examination has been finished, I say to the mother,
"This is a matter to be worried about. This child's brain, thyroid,
digestive organs, every cell in her body, cannot function properly
without the normal amount of oxygen; and the oxygen cannot get
to these cells in all parts of her body without blood; and this child
has only half as much blood or hemoglobin as she needs. So you see
she can't get much more than half as much oxygen as she needs and
her heart tries to bring this up by beating faster and her lungs by
breathing faster. Every muscle in her body is impoverished and that
is why we get this little murmur. The body acts as a whole, and you
can see why she will not play as she should and why she cries so
much. Her muscles are soft and weak throughout her entire body.
She cannot make blood, and without blood none of her glands function right for lack of nourishment. So you can see her problem.

"Now what can be done about it? You can never correct this with
vitamins or iron although they will help. Only a good system will
save this child. You really don't know who this child is potentially.
She may be a great mother, teacher, or someone to make a better
world if she only has a chance. We can't afford to let this little girl
down, and you are the one to save her.

"She was never supposed to regulate her life, but you were made
her mother to show her a way and give her what is best for her.
When you were a little girl, did your mother let you sleep half the
morning and eat when and what you pleased?" "No, my mother had
too much to do to put up with that. We had to get up and eat

breakfast with my father at daylight." "Why do you not give your child a chance like your mother gave you?

"First, we must get her teeth fixed, having the ones that are abscessed pulled, and the others filled. Get the bad tonsils out. The crypts in her tonsils harbor organisms and pus that cannot be cleared up by medicine. We see children with bad teeth or large infected tonsils who have rheumatic fever and continue to have attacks. We can culture the throat and find no evidence of the hemolytic streptococcus, but when the tonsils are removed and a culture is made from a cross section of the crypt, we may find the hemolytic streptococcus that is causing the rheumatic fever. With her big glands we know she is harboring an infection in the crypts of her tonsils and we cannot get her well until we clear up all her infections. Your child need not have had all these bad teeth. You could have saved her teeth and your money if you had done two simple things: had not permitted her to eat between meals and had not given her carbonated drinks." "I thought if she had plenty of milk her teeth would be good." "The cow, horse, lion, and other mammals do not have milk after the nursing period and their teeth are not decayed. Milk does not have anything to do with decay; it is caused by the etching of the teeth by an acid from the carbonated drinks or an acid caused by constant food decay between teeth or mouth breathing or vomiting. After the teeth and tonsils are cleared up, I want you to try out this routine for three months and then come back to see me. I am not going to give you a prescription for something to buy. Just do what your mother did for you. Now the iron and vitamins might hasten this recovery but I want you to see just what you can do with a child on a good schedule.

"She is to get up in the morning when you and your husband get up. You should prepare a good country breakfast of meat or eggs, grits, farina, oatmeal, or corn meal mush; hot cakes or bread; raw fruit and cooked fruit; water to drink. This meal is to be at seven o'clock. The meal should be served with all members of the family at the table at the same time. There should be a blessing. There should be no talk about food and no suggestion made as to eating the food. As soon as Papa finishes, clear the table. She is to have no food or drink except water until twelve-thirty. If Papa is not home for this meal, serve what was left from the previous evening meal. You should cook with this in mind, so there will be enough to serve you and your child a meal at twelve-thirty. Never make the lunch just sandwiches and soup. Give no drinks with this meal except water. There should be no food or drinks except water until six o'clock. That meal should be a meat, a green vegetable, some starch, a cooked fruit, a raw fruit, a raw vegetable as a salad, a whole grain bread, with water to drink.

"She is to have no naps during the day but should rest for one hour after lunch. Then she will be ready to go to bed at six-thirty to seven o'clock. Give this a trial. You and your little girl try living together and let her help you and you be ready to help her with her projects and problems. Teach her to sew and help you bake, read to her after lunch, teach her how to create her amusements and to make her dolls and doll dresses and you will be a happy mother and she will find out the most important thing in a child's life—that she has been born with a good guide."

If the mother carries out the schedule for three months, she always comes back with this statement, "Doctor, I never knew I had such a fine child. She is a joy and we have so much fun. We have no bedtime problems and no eating problems."

Life is such a short day, and it is hard to see why we are not willing to give our children a chance by doing this day right. The greatest need of today or any day is parents who love their children enough to give them a chance to have a good body, good manners, a deep respect for others, and an ever-thankful attitude toward God and man. All this has to be taught. From conception to six years of age is the most important time in a human life and parents must not miss one opportunity to make this period as perfect as possible. We may be casual about some things; but we cannot be casual about this little baby who has come to live with us. We have no way to know who he is or where he is going, but this short stay with us must prepare him for the life he is to live, and we must make it so perfect he will never have reason to look back on this time as a curse, but on the contrary . . . as a great blessing.

After a child is six, if we have not made him develop a complex by constant nagging, talking, forcing and bribing, he will eat well and start a fast period of growth for two years. The appetite levels off then, and he makes a gradual gain and eats a moderate amount until he reaches adolescence when the appetite becomes enormous—more so for boys than girls; but both eat well if they practice the laws of good health and do not eat between meals so the stomach can empty as it should. There is never a time in the life of a human being when he should abuse his body. His body is the only house he will ever have to live in, so, if he wants to be happy, he must learn from birth to keep the house clean and in good repair.

My philosophy is that if a mother runs her house like a man runs a good business, it will be a success. Building a child is the biggest business on earth.

The Anemic Child

What is really the trouble in a country like ours when we have so many undernourished children with an abundance of good food and thousands of books on nutrition? It is not because people cannot get food. For some fifty years I have given one day a week to a clinic trying to help the so-called underprivileged child, and I can say from experience that most of these children could have enough food to keep them in good health if the mothers would fix it and serve it right. Why are we seeing so many anemic people, both children and adults? I read an article recently written by an internal medicine man saying a seventy per cent hemoglobin seems to be the normal now, and that was about the highest he could get.

Of the new patients that come to my office and the ones I see in the clinic, I would say that seventy per cent hemoglobin would be above the average and fifty per cent would not be uncommon. It is a frequent experience to find children with hemoglobin as low as thirty per cent.

My practice changed considerably thirty years ago when we moved out twelve miles from town and one mile from any kind of commercial transportation. In town I had what I called a luxury practice. I would see the new baby as soon as he was born and then at regular intervals until the child became a teenager. The parents became friends and there was not too much sickness. These fine little children made up the greater part of my practice, and I did not see as much tragedy as I do now.

My office being so far out in the country and hard to get to, parents would come with their children only when they had a problem they could not get solved nearer home. Many of these children had been the rounds of the doctors, and perhaps to the chiropractor; and then they would come out to see if a little old woman doctor might be able to help. This is not being said in levity. They will say, "Doctor, this child has had penicillin shots until he looks like a pin cushion, and still he is sick. We have been doctored and adjusted until the money has given out . . . and we have come to you as the last resort." The parents are often the type of people who want the doctor to keep the child well and happy, and let them pay the bill and go free.

No doctor can help these little children until the parents are willing to give them a chance, and that chance has to come from the parents. These children can be made well and happy if the parents are willing to work out a good way of life for them.

When a child has a thirty per cent or seventy per cent hemoglobin, he has a seventy per cent or thirty per cent deficiency in every cell in his body. The cells cannot live without blood and in order for the cells to produce at their maximum, they must have the maximum amount of blood. I see a child come in with thirty per cent hemoglobin whose hair is dry, stiff and uncontrollable; skin yellow, puffy and dry; muscles soft; a heart murmur; irritable and hard to live with. Or, this child may be very good since he does not have enough pep to be bad. I remember one father bringing in three little girls one night, all as pale as death. I asked him why he brought them and he said they were just too good—that no children should be as quiet and docile as they were.

Most of these children are fat, and, seeing them for the first time, you would think of a thyroid deficiency which is actually true. The child's thyroid glands trying to produce with a thirty per cent hemoglobin cannot do a normal job any more than the muscles of his heart can do a perfect job when they cannot snap back in place as they should because they are deficient in oxygen that has to come by way of the blood. The thyroid lacks oxygen in the same proportion as the blood is deficient and that is true of every cell in the body. Every organ in the body falls short of its normal activity, digestion is poor, and the organs that make blood cannot make blood without blood.

When a child is anemic, his power to cure himself and to be at his best physically and mentally is in direct proportion to the amount of oxygen which is carried by the blood, and blood cannot be made without the proper food and the elimination of any infection that would cause anemia. Reading article after article and hearing a great deal of talk about all the sure cures for anemia with iron and vitamins and different ways to build up the blood, one comes to the point and says, "Why take medicine to bring the blood up? Why not stop the reason for the anemia?" There are types of anemia that require constant medication but that is not what I am talking about. I am talking about secondary anemia, the type we see every day that can be corrected. Fighting anemia is just like lend-lease; we can't help a person if that person does not start by helping himself, otherwise there would be no end to the help we would have to give. If we give medicine for the anemia and do not remove the cause, the anemia returns when the medicine is stopped. Thousands of children and adults are being treated that way today.

When we take a history on anemic children, we find they all run about the same story. "Well, what is your trouble?" "Doctor, this child is sick all the time, will not eat, sleeps poorly, cries a great deal, is irritable, is constipated, and I just can't understand why my child has to be so much trouble. I have tried all the doctors and all kinds of medicine. "Was it breast or bottle fed?" As a rule, the answer to this question is that the baby was bottle fed. "Did the baby do well at first?" "Yes, for the first six months he was fine," or the answer may be that he has never eaten well. "Let's go over your schedule for a day." "Oh, I don't have any schedule; I just do as the child de-mands." "Well, what time does the child get up?" "At no special time; sometimes about nine o'clock and sometimes about ten o'clock." "What will he eat for breakfast?" "Nothing." Then there is some backing up. She will say he has a little cereal and milk, or jelly and bread, and maybe a glass of milk, or about anything she can get him to eat. "When will he eat again?" "About twelve noon." "What will he eat then?" "Practically nothing except his milk." "When will he have a nap"?" "About two o'clock. I give him a bottle to go to sleep on." "When will he be awake?" "About three or four o'clock." "Do you feed him when he gets up"?" "Yes, a bottle and some cookies." "When will he eat supper?" "About six o'clock." "What will he eat then?" "Nothing much; maybe a little meat and potatoes and his bottle." "When will he go to bed?" "About ten o'clock and I give him a bottle to go to sleep with. He nurses the bottle about all night."

These "about" mothers are the reasons for a great number of the problems of anemia in children. Medicine is not what an anemic child needs—he needs a good mother and he needs nourishing food. He also needs a thorough examination. If there is a bad tooth, it should be removed or the infection cleared up. If he has big infected tonsils, they should be removed. A child with big cervical glands cannot be helped until the infection is removed. If there is a cough, the reason should be found and cleared up. If there is constant discharge from the nose, the child is sick and the cause should be found. Fever is a good sign of infection and the kidneys may be at fault. Every effort should be made to find any infection that could be contributing to the anemia, but in the meantime the child should be put on food that will furnish the iron and vitamins and everything it takes to build up blood.

With anemia, metabolism is greatly handicapped. With the "about" mother, the child never has a normal diet and as the child develops anemia, metabolism is decreased, activity is less, appetite becomes poor, anxiety on the mother's part increases, and then there is forced feeding or the child is allowed to nibble all day. With anxiety on the mother's part comes rebellion on the child's part, and a vicious circle is formed. The baby stays on the bottle or breast for months, in some cases—years, just because he will not eat; and he will not eat because he is getting the milk, and also because the mother has said he will not eat, and she lets him eat when he pleases and what he pleases to keep him alive. These children all look alike. They take a great amount of milk from the bottle or otherwise, and some of them come in with a hemoglobin as low as ten per cent.

The lower animals do not take milk after the sucking period. The cat has milk for six weeks, the sea lion fifteen days, the dog not more than twelve weeks, the calf for a very short time, and on and on it goes. All animals wean their young as soon as they are able to eat, and they never have milk again, They never have bad teeth and do not develop anemia like the human race. Squirrels have milk for a short time and never again and they can open a hickory nut with their teeth. If a cat is fed only milk after it is weaned, it will develop severe anemia. This is true of all domestic animals. A year-old German shepherd that has been fed as a dog should be fed on meat and vegetables will have one hundred per cent hemoglobin and six million red cells. If on the same diet one quart of cow's milk a day is added, in two months the hemoglobin will have dropped thirty per cent and the red cells in the same proportion. If the dog is put on a diet of cow's milk only, he will not live two months. I know because I have made this experiment. The exact reason for this reduction in red corpuscles and hemoglobin and the marked increase in white corpuscles is not known, but it does occur; and it is not because the animal is not taking other food, for dogs and cats with their regular diet have still developed anemia. But in the animals that are fed milk only, the anemia develops much faster and is far more severe.

This is evident in the pregnant mothers of today. They usually eat well after the first three months, but some develop severe anemia before the nine months are up. These mothers are often advised to drink milk to make the baby better and supply extra calcium but if the diet is proper, the milk not only is not needed but will be harmful.

In the nineteen-twenties and early thirties there was much written and said about rickets, and the diagnosis was made many times with these symptoms: a child overweight, with a big pot belly; skin dry, rough, thick, pale; hair dry; sad face; big square head; bowed legs and arms; large ankles and wrists which gave the joints a double appearance; and the ends of the ribs enlarged. (This is not to be confused with the disease, renal rickets.) We know that cow's milk has about ten times as much calcium and phosphorus as human milk and if the child consumes great quantities of cow's milk, the calcium and phosphorus have to be stored in the body or excreted because the body will maintain a blood chemistry as nearly normal as possible. With this great amount of calcium and phosphorus, and a normal blood calcium and phosphorus, the excess may be the reason for abnormal development in the growth of the long bones and the skull. This condition that is so often called rickets is not rickets at all but is caused by too much milk. When the milk is removed from the diet and the child is fed meat, vegetables, fruit and cereal, and given water to drink, he shows great improvement in a few weeks, without any medication.

One observation I have made over the years is that when we open the long bones of a chicken that has been fed large amounts of milk, we will find the medullary cavity filled with a complete network of fine spicules of bone that almost obliterates the medullary cavity and decreases the amount of marrow until it is almost dry. In a normal chicken that has not been fed milk, this marrow can be removed almost in one piece and there is very little evidence of bone formation in the medullary cavity. The marrow is a long, very vascular mass that resembles a blood clot. I have never been able to compare the medullary cavities of the long bones of a baby that has had great quantities of cow's milk with the medullary cavities of a baby that had human milk and was weaned at seven months and then given a normal diet of meat, vegetables, fruit and cereal. I am sure, however, that in the case of the anemic, milk-fed child, the medullary cavities are filled with fine spicules of bone from the excess calcium and phosphorus consumed, and that this is the reason it takes so long to get a normal hemoglobin. All of this excess bone has to be reabsorbed and the marrow has to grow back to the normal amount.

I am sure that the thing we have called rickets many times has been a milk sickness. I have never observed this type of so-called rickets in the little emaciated children who should be the ones to have rickets, if it is due to a deficiency, as these children may be so starved that they have pellagra and still have no sign of rickets by X-ray or physical examination. All of these children with marked anemia, lemon color, bowed legs and arms, big square heads, big wrists and ankles, and pot belly, will clear up on good food when the milk is omitted and they are fed on a five and one-half hour schedule.

The diet I have used with hundreds of these children has been meat with each meal, beef, lamb, chicken, fish, liver, meat base formula; vegetables three times a day, blackeyed peas, cabbage, okra, broccoli, cauliflower, squash, beets, green beans, et cetera; fruit, bananas, apples, pears, prunes. The starch consists of whole grain cereal or sweet potato and some white potato (but not too much), corn meal mush (which is one of the best), whole grain breads, brown rice, and no drinks except water. For the first month the gain in hemoglobin will be between ten per cent and twelve per cent—not very fast—but after the child has made enough blood and the bone marrow has had a chance to return to normal, the increase in hemoglobin becomes much faster.

The mother must know that the progress at first will be slow, and she must understand that a child cannot build blood without blood. With a hemoglobin between ten per cent and fifiy per cent, the making of blood is ninety to fifty per cent less than the normal rate. Once the mother understands the condition of her child and she is given a good schedule to go by, she can soon see that the child did not need a doctor but he needed a good mother who was willing to build for her child a body that would be able to function at its maximum capacity. I never tell a mother that a hundred per cent hemoglobin will make her child an A-plus student, but I can assure her it will help her child's brain to function at its full capacity.

It is almost a daily occurrence for a mother to bring in a school child with a complaint going like this: "Doctor, the teacher called me in and she thinks my child must be sick for he has lost interest, does not finish his work, is not happy, and seems sleepy." Most of these children are not well, and they are doing as well as they feel like doing. As a rule, I find on examination some infection and anemia and on questioning the mother find that the child has no regular schedule and the diet is poor. To me, one of the most gratifying things in life is to see these little children who are talked about and really fussed at about their school work given a chance, and I have seen many make good students when I could get the mother to feed them right, sleep them right, help them each night with their school work, and tell them they are somebody and not run them down. A child can't learn if he is anemic and sick, and a child can't learn if his parents are always telling him how sorry he is. We should build our child's ego and make him believe that we believe he is somebody.

We must always look for the obvious in our child. When we are trying to help our child, we must not try to make him play, but we must make him feel well enough to want to play. We must not try to make him learn, but make him feel well enough so he can learn. We must not make a child eat, but make him well enough to want to eat, and this is all so simple if we will just think a little and know how the body works. And no matter how much we would like to change his body, it still operates on a natural system that cannot be changed. The child must have the right food at the right time in the right atmosphere. We should avoid over-stressing food. Some families spend large amounts of money for all kinds of sweet drinks, milk, dry cereal, cookies, and many other things that cost money that could be spent for good meat, vegetables, fruit, and starches composed of whole grain breads and potatoes. There are many products on the market today to make somebody rich and to destroy the person that is foolish enough to buy them. I hear parents in my office and in the clinic talking about how expensive it is to live and how little they have and, as a rule, if they will go over the budget, they will find they are spending more to destroy their bodies than they are spending to build them up.

To sum this up, first we must find out why a child is anemic and how the condition can be corrected. We must be sure all infections are cleared up. There may be a chronic condition of the chest, ears, throat, sinus, bad tonsils, and we can't build up the child until we have cleared up the infection. Sometimes a mixed vaccine given for these chronic infections speeds up the antibody formation and shortens the time. There are many other types of infection that must be looked for, such as kidney, heart, intestinal, glandular, and digestive; and we must remember that man has never been able to cure man and keep him well, but that has to be done in man. We can stop an infection but as soon as the medicine we have is gone, the person can be sick again if he has not built antibodies in his own body to protect him against infections.

So we come to the next and most important step in preventing anemia, which is to feed the body right, keep the body outdoors as much as possible, exercise the body every day, and never put anything in the body that would make it less efficient. The care of the body should be man's first interest, for there is where he lives and a man can be no better than the house he lives in, and man himself has to keep this house. We must teach our children from birth the importance of the human body, their bodies and the bodies of all the people they come in contact with. We must teach mothers that they are the most important persons on earth to their children and that their job should be met with joy and not with a feeling of punishment; that it is a privilege to be a mother, not a task. Little children can be salvaged before it is too late if mothers can be shown how they are destroying their lives. A mother has no way to know who this child is that she has been privileged to feed and train and prepare to run the race of life. Maybe that is good, for if a mother knew she was giving birth to a great surgeon, she might over-protect him, and if she knew he would be a demon, she might not protect him enough. With good care I have seen the school grades of children change completely and homes change from dens of chaos to wonderful places to live. We can't change the inborn capacity of a person, but we can develop what is there to its maximum.

When a mother sees that her child is not well or is not behaving in a normal manner and is not happy, she should begin to ask these questions: Am I feeding this child right? Are the meals spaced as they should be? Does the child eat between meals? How much food does this child consume that would help build up his hemoglobin? Have I let this child get into the habit of telling me what he wants? Was he weaned at seven months or is he still on the bottle? How much milk does he consume each day? How much of his meal is made up of starches? Are the meals served in an attractive manner? Is the meal time a happy time? How much nagging is done at the table? Do I form an audience for my child to act for at the table? Is all the attention at meal time directed to my child's eating? Am I treating my child at the table like I would want to be treated? Do I serve a full and balanced meal or am I making the meal of snacks? Do I serve a sweet drink with the meal? Do I serve a glass of milk that the child can consume before his plate is served? Do I try to bribe my child at the table by saying if he will eat his meal, I will give him some cake? Does my child feel that it is a privilege to eat and not a task? Are my table manners and eating habits a good example for my child? Is my house so filled with tobacco smoke my child cannot enjoy the aroma of my cooking? (This item has played a major role in feeding problems. The wonderful aroma of food whets the appetite more than any known tonic and there are thousands of little children who never get to enjoy this aroma especially in the winter when both parents are smoking and the house is closed up.) Is my child worrying himself to death about my behavior? (I hear this too often in my office: "Doctor, I just can't eat, I am so worried about my parents. My mother and father drink too much, smoke too much; Mother comes to school and goes to market in pants that are too tight, she wears make-up that makes her look what she is not, and the other kids think bad things about Mother. If she would only be a person I could be proud of and brag about, I would be happy; but with my worrying I just can't make the food go down.") Is my child getting enough sleep?

After analyzing all these questions and we are sure our child's trouble is not caused by anything we are doing or not doing, then we should see a doctor, for the child is probably sick. A normal child is happy and will eat, and will not develop anemia without a reason.

♂ ♀

4. Thumb sucking

Thumb sucking has caused a great deal of controversy, as well as anxiety, among mothers, fathers, grandmothers, and even grandfathers. This act keeps family and friends in constant conversation when they see a baby enjoying his thumb.

If we read some of our noted psychiatrists, we will be led to believe that everything in life is built around sex; and sucking has been one act that has entered into the discussion. When the cigarette habit was getting a good start, there were some hints by the psychiatrists that the reason a person would suck on a cigarette was because he did not get enough sucking as a child. As time has gone on and so many people are sucking on some form of tobacco to get the nicotine, that idea has been given up and now we don't try to find an excuse for their sucking. We know they smoke because they like the effects of the tobacco.

On the theory that sucking has something to do with sex, a parent would be afraid to make any move or correction of the child for fear of upsetting his sex life, But parents should and must come back to the old-fashioned exercise of thinking a little for themselves. They must know that they have knowledge and wisdom and the power to think and that there is something in them that tells them right from wrong in all matters of life. They must take time to talk these matters over among themselves and never go for help until they are sure they can't solve their own problems. In many cases when we can't solve our own problems, the trouble is we want to do the thing that is wrong and we go out for help, hoping that the person we consult will tell us to do what we want to do, and then we can put the blame on this person for our wrongdoing.

When we ask someone to help us, we must know how well he is prepared to help us make our decisions. A century ago there were no baby doctors, no psychiatrists to guide the mothers, yet at that time great and honest people lived and produced great people and great works. The words "juvenile delinquent" and "immaturity" had not become common expressions. I read recently in a medical journal this statement: "Infantile experience as an important dynamic factor in the determination of adult personality has received little attention until recent years." There could never have been a more exaggerated statement. Since the beginning of time, mothers have worked from the day of conception until the day their boy or girl leaves home trying to get into that child all the things that would make a better life and better preparation for parenthood.

"Train up a child in the way he should go," was not said yesterday, but almost as long ago as we have recorded history. I will make this statement and I am sure it is true: The mothers of long ago were better teachers of their children than the mothers of today. They had more time for the home, and there was very little outside influence. So the more we read, the more confused we get.

A mother was in my office a short time ago with a poor little boy who looked as bad as a child could look. I checked him over and then tried to advise her as to a way of life that I thought would help the little boy. After I finished writing out a schedule, she said to me, "I have been to ten doctors before I came to you and every doctor has told me something different. Who am I to believe is right?" I said to her, "If you ask ten different women how to bake a cake, you will get ten different answers. Whom would you follow?" She thought for a moment, then smiled and said, "I would have to decide myself."

The young mother and father should just settle down and do a little thinking for themselves. What happens to a little puppy when you step on his tail? He runs to his mother to nurse. He thinks sucking will stop the pain. This has no connection whatsoever with sex. He has been hurt, he has pain, and he thinks sucking will stop the pain. He wants comfort. He knows this act of sucking works when he has a hunger pain and he thinks it will work with all pain.

The same is true of a little baby. As soon as he is born, he starts swallowing air, and when his stomach fills with air, it hurts. Instinctively he thinks sucking will stop the pain, not knowing that every time he sucks, he swallows more air which causes more pain. Thus, it is easy and natural for him to find his thumb or perhaps the pacifier in some of the more "modern" cases where the mother is afraid the baby will suffer from a frustration predicted by somebody if he does not get in a certain quota of sucking. Or she may give him the pacifier to shut him up. Or perhaps she will allow him to nurse the breast or give him the bottle all day or night.

Considering these three methods of trying to appease, let's think about the nursing first. The mother reads in a book that she should go by demand feedings and nurse as often and as long as the baby cries, so she lets him nurse, if he cries, to prevent frustration. Now I can't believe that a woman who has nursed a baby could go along with that. In one day's time her breast would be so sore she could not stand to have the baby nurse.

Not many years ago a very smart man came to lecture in our town on "Child Psychology" and his subject was "Thumb Sucking and Its Effect on the Child." His suggestion was the pacifier. Since he was an out-of-town visitor, naturally he left a great number of converts. If a speaker is from "far off," what he says is always important; or if we read it in the papers or see it on television, the effect is the same. So when he left our town, the sale of pacifiers increased. I have often wondered if he didn't own the company that manufactured pacifiers, as I understand that he gave up pediatrics soon after that and went into another type of medicine.

If a person would think, he would not agree with the idea of a pacifier at all. A pacifier is made of rubber and is hard in comparison with the human nipple which is the softest part of the body so it will not irritate the baby's tongue and mouth. The skin on the baby's thumb is soft and could not harm the baby's tongue and mouth. The friction between the rubber pacifier and the baby's tongue takes all the epithelium cells off the tongue and the tongue gets a smooth red appearance; the taste buds are flat; and the tongue is sore. Then thrush begins to develop, which makes the baby more uncomfortable; and he sucks more and more, thinking that the sucking will stop the pain. So he keeps the pacifier in his mouth all the time and continues to rub his tongue on the hard rubber.

A baby was in my office recently that had been on a pacifier all his life and his mouth was raw inside; also the buttocks and all the finger nails were infected from Monilia (thrush) caused by the pacifier.

This condition can cause death in a baby and it is so unnecessary. Thumb sucking could not cause this. I have seen a mother, who has spent hours fixing the bottles and clothes so the baby will not get an infection, take a pacifier out of her pocket or pocketbook and put it in the baby's mouth. Then I have seen her take the pacifier out of the baby's mouth and put it in her pocketbook or place it on the table, never washing it at all. Many of these pacifier babies have diarrhoea which the mother cannot understand because she keeps the bottles clean, but she never thinks of how nasty the pacifier is.

So the best way to stop this awful thing is to throw the pacifier in the trash and let the baby cry for a while—then the show is over. I suggested this once at a meeting and a young doctor came up with the word "frustration." I replied with the following statement, "From the time a child is born, he must be taught that he can't have everthing he wants. He comes to live with his parents, and not his parents to live with him. He must be taught that he must do as they say as long as he lives in their house, and when he gets a house of his own, they in turn must not interfere with the way he runs his home. He must know that they love him enough to hear him cry if he is crying for something that will harm him, and a mother who really loves her baby would not do anything to that baby that would harm him. It seems to me that all the 'pacifier mothers' look alike, and they have the most insecure babies."

This same young doctor made the suggestion that we should take the pacifier away gradually. The answer to that comes from a story about one of my little patients who said he was going to cut off his puppy's tail. He was going to cut off just a little piece each day so it would not hurt so bad. I say the way to deal with children is to do the things for them that are best now and never bring up the subject again.

Children are not frustrated with definite acts or orders. The children that are upset are those that never know what to expect of their parents. The parents will let them act one way today and nothing is said or done, but tomorrow they object or inhibit. Children must be inhibited to teach them self-control and to make them see how their acts affect them and their fellow man. We can't afford to teach children that every desire they have must be satisfied at any cost. So the pacifier is a trouble maker. In the skin of the thumb there are anti-bodies that kill microbes and the thumb is attached to the arm that can remove it at will, whereas in the case of a newborn the pacifier has to remain in his mouth until the mother removes it. The "paci-fier" mothers all seem to follow the same pattern. They are not prob-lem solvers. They stick a pacifier in the baby's mouth to shut him up. They let him have papa's best tools. They let him stay home from school because he cries. This type mother has destroyed many chil-dren. Mothers should never pacify but love their children enough to help them solve their problems .

Now let us consider the effect of thumb sucking on the mouth. I have studied faces for years and I have never seen a person with "bucked teeth" who did not have a short upper lip. Our teeth are kept in place by our lips and tongue. If anyone interested will make a study of this in a group of people, I am sure he will agree with me. If he will make a study of this in his own mouth, he will notice when he sucks or swallows, his lips pull in and his tongue pushes out. Now if the lip is stronger than the push of the tongue, the teeth are forced back which gives a flat appearance to the mouth. If the upper lip is short and not as strong as the push of the tongue, we have protruding teeth. Thumb sucking will change the shape of the teeth in a child but when the sucking is stopped, if the lips and tongue are in normal balance, the teeth will soon return to the normal position. So "bucked teeth" are the end result of abnormal lip and tongue force and are not caused by the act of thumb sucking.

The way I handle thumb sucking is never to encourage or dis-courage it. I teach the parents never to bring the subject up or start pulling out the thumb and making an issue of the matter.

If a young baby has a stomach ache, he has a reason to suck his thumb and the cause of the stomach ache can be determined if the doctor and mother will try to find it.

It is not unusual for a baby to be born with a partial obstruction which would cause pain that would start thumb sucking. Or, if he is born addicted to alcohol, tobacco, or drugs because his mother used these things during pregnancy, he may start sucking his thumb, thinking this will ease his discomfort. Eczema also makes a baby uncomfortable and this could induce the habit. In other words, every baby that sucks his thumb starts it because he is hungry or uncomfortable. With a correct diet and the elimination of other things that cause discomfort, the sucking will not become a habit.

The only reason I would favor the breaking of the thumb-sucking habit is to eliminate pin worms. At about two years of age children begin to play with other children and other children's toys that may be covered with pin worm eggs. The average child over two years that continues to suck his thumb, bite his nails, or put his hands in his mouth has pin worms. The eggs of these worms are everywhere and they stick to the hands. I have had wonderful success with older children who suck their thumbs or bite their nails by explaining to them how impossible it is to get rid of the worms as long as they keep putting their fingers in their mouths. But I always tell them to make up their own minds, that if they don't want the worms, they will have to give up the nails and thumb. Nagging is the devil's best weapon and the average person will not discontinue what he is doing if he is continually nagged. If I push a person, he will push me back, and when I quit, he will quit. We never act without an audience and when the audience disappears, the show is over. This is true of man from birth to the grave.

I am not saying we should never force a child or inflict physical punishment. Every command parents give a child must be carried through or the child loses respect for them, but there are a few things we can't make a child do. We can't make him eat, sleep, or eliminate, nor can we make him stop sucking his thumb. He can suck it under the cover or out back of the house. So the best way to stop this act is to tell the child the truth about the harm of thumb sucking, and never nag. If we as parents would think and consider carefully the harm done by nagging and giving commands that are not carried through, we would change our approach and help our children to help themselves.

In summary, for the first three months of life a baby swallows air and has colic and the thumb is used as a pacifier . . . as a desire for comfort. After three months the thumb will go if the diet is correct and the baby has recovered from his addiction to alcohol, nicotine, caffeine, or any other stimulants or sedatives. But if he has used his thumb with his colic, or his upset mental and physical state—caused by his addiction to the things his mother took before he was born, he goes for his thumb again when he feels the discomfort from his teeth as they start coming through. It feels good to rub his sore gums with his little soft thumb. Now this continues until the two-year molars are through, for there is never a time from five months of age to two years that the gums are not swollen.

At the end of the second year if the thumb is still used, the parents are beginning to talk about the act and pull the thumb out, make all kinds of threats, and use the most harmful statement that can be used before a child, saying, "I can't stop my child from sucking his thumb." When the parents say, "We can't stop him," he has to keep on because they have confessed he is greater and more powerful than they are. So the thumb sucking becomes an issue. He sucks because it creates a situation that provides him an audience and as long as there is an audience, there is acting. This acting will not end at the end of the negative period of the child's life if there is still an audience. I had one boy patient that sucked his thumb for twenty-one years or until he was married. His parents had made such an issue of it, he could not afford to stop.

When a mother comes to me with this problem after the child is two years old, I assure her that she is the cause of the trouble and that she must convince the child that she does not care if he does use his thumb. And the way to do that is to have him come in each day, wash his hands clean, sit on a chair and suck his thumb for at least thirty minutes, making this statement to him, "You have got to suck your thumb thirty minutes, each day by the clock." But we must be sure that we are ready to give up our nagging and be sure we are sincere in the act. This will never fail if carried out at two years if we are firm and always follow through. At five years, if we explain to the child that when he sucks his thumb or puts his unwashed hands in his mouth, he will have worms and say no more, the act stops.

We must remember that "bucked teeth" result from an anatomical defect and that they are not caused by thumb sucking. I have looked for years trying to see an adult sitting in church or in any other audience sucking his thumb and I have never seen the first one, so we can be sure they will stop sometime. We should give up our worrying and nagging, and use our time to teach our child a good way of life. We must give him a chance by being the parents we would have liked our parents to be or the parent we want our child to be.

♂ ♀

5. Clothes

The human body has worn some form of clothes as far back as history has been recorded. If we believe the Old Testament, clothes were first worn in the Garden of Eden after Adam and Eve had eaten of the forbidden fruit. They knew they were nude, and they were ashamed and covered their bodies. Since that day, clothes have played a great part in distinguishing between the rich and the poor, the good and the bad, different cults, races, and ways of life.

When a baby is born, he should be clothed, according to the temperature, in soft cotton or linen that is sufficient to keep him warm enough or cool enough. He should never wear clothes that do not absorb moisture or do not fit close to the body. Closeness is very important, for the baby has been held tight for nine months and he is much happier if he is swaddled.

During the first six months of a baby's life the clothes, if they are soft and comfortable, will not affect the child's life. They may be any color or be made in any style. Boys and girls may be dressed alike. The clothes may be long or short; the only thing that matters is that they are comfortable.

At six months there is a definite change. The clothes must be short enough to allow the child freedom to crawl. At this time the style or color, or the fact that they may be girl's or boy's clothes does not affect the child. All he wants is comfort and the freedom to crawl.

At one year or at the time when a child is first walking, there is a big change. A boy seems to know he is a boy, and a girl seems to know she is a girl. When a little girl is dressed in a beautiful dress, she will show a marked feeling of pleasure, and she knows she is beautiful. She likes to look in the mirror and admire herself. A little boy seems to throw his chest out when he is dressed like a boy with his hair cut like a boy's. He will admire his looks as much as a little girl admires her looks. A little boy who is made to wear long hair and girls' clothes after one year never seems to get over that curse. A boy who after one year is dressed like a girl as a rule is a bad child. If this is carried into the negative period of a boy's life—from two to six—he becomes destructive and wants to fight all the time to show people that although he may dress or wear his hair like a girl, his parents can't make him act like a girl.

When one of these little children is brought into my office for the first time, wearing long curls, white high-top shoes, and fancy clothes, I may say, "What a beautiful little girl." And the mother, always with a moronic-type smile, will say, "Oh, no. This is my son. He is not a girl and if he stays around long, you will find that out. He hates to be called a girl."

And this is true. If we are around him very long, we will soon think he is demon-possessed because he must show us that his appearance has caused people to pass the wrong judgment on him, and he must prove to the world he is not a girl. I have had the opportunity to follow these children from birth to adult life and they never seem to get over this experience. One would say that a mother who would do such a thing to a child is not a normal mother. I am sure that no normal mother would ever do anything to a child to handicap him, but there are many selfish or abnormal women who have babies, and their children do not have a chance to develop normally. They are under the curse of a bad parent, the most unfortunate thing on earth. The stigma of being called a female when one is a male cannot be forgotten if a child is subjected to this for a long time. Many females seem to be dissatisfied with their sex, but I have never seen a male who would change into a female. So a boy should be dressed as a boy after he is one year old. His hair should be cut in a boy's style, and he should never be referred to as looking like a girl.

At about two and a half years, a little girl has become quite clothes-conscious. She will put on her mother's high-heeled shoes and dress up like a lady to play. She will cry to wear her most feminine dresses all the time. While she has these on, she behaves like a little lady and talks nicely and is very gentle. But when the mother decides the dresses are too much trouble and begins to dress her like a boy, she acts like a bad boy. She will talk loudly, climb, throw things, and will get all dirty. She is acting the way she is dressed. This is as true as life. All human beings are greatly influenced by the kind of clothes they wear or don't wear.

When my little niece was about three years old, the blue jeans fad for girls had just started. She was a beautiful little girl with long curls and big blue eyes. She was a well-trained little lady, very gracious and polite to everyone, and was a child who spoke in a most correct manner. One day she asked her mother to get her some blue jeans like the little girl's next door. Her mother complied with my niece's wishes and bought the blue jeans and thought she looked cute in them. But her first day in the jeans was an eye-opener for my sister. This beautiful well-mannered child was completely changed. One day ran like this. She was on top of the garage throwing rocks at the children next door. She talked loud and a little sassy. She used a stick for a gun and was a little gangster in a big way. Her hair was not in curls any more; her face was black and her hands were dirty. She was a typical example of a girl who tries to dress and act like a boy. She went far beyond the worst of boys to show she was a real boy. One day was all this child had in blue jeans, and she was punished more that day than she had ever been in all her life.

Children are going to act the way they are dressed. It is not the way the clothes are made that is important for in some countries the males wear long dresses or kilts. It is what the clothes represent that matters. A boy with a cowboy outfit talks about killing, robbing, and riding horses for he has come to think those are the things a cowboy does. A boy in a neat suit talks about things his father does and acts the part of a man when he is dressed in that attire. Little boys never get into much mischief in church or school-going clothes if they are dressed properly for these two occasions. Children when dressed like adults act like the adults they are dressed like. We can watch little girls at play. They will get a low-necked, tight-fitting, black dress and in a few minutes they are using sticks for cigarettes and something they can find that will represent a cocktail. They are very wicked in their little minds. They will sit with their legs crossed so they can expose as much of their legs as possible, and they puff and drink with the greatest glee. Then let these little girls get into their mothers' house dresses and aprons and they will start making mud pies and playing house.

Parents should be careful about how they dress their children and, more important, how they dress themselves as an example of a good way of life. The child of today is exposed to all types of people every day through television, newspapers, magazines, books, and neighbors. The parental influence will have to be stronger than ever and more exacting if we are to give our children a chance to make the best out of their lives. We play this thing we call life a long time before it becomes real.

Parents could learn a lot about themselves if they would take time to listen to their children at play.

I am not saying that children should not be permitted to play and create their own interpretations of the adults they know or read about, but the trouble comes when the parents encourage games that will cause trouble later. For instance, a parent I knew had one beautiful daughter. The second baby was to be a boy, they would say, and they made plans for a boy. But when the baby came, it was another beautiful girl. Their friends teased them, and they laughed and called this little girl their "boy." They dressed her like a boy, and she had boy toys. They had lots of fun calling her a boy and would continue to say, "I just can't get her to wear girl clothes or to play with dolls or play with girls. We have to buy her boy toys and boy clothes."

This little girl was just as beautiful as her sister at birth, but the parents continued to talk about her masculine behavior and to confess that they could not do anything about it. At twenty years old she was still wearing men's clothes and a man's haircut. She walked like a man. Women were afraid of her, and men had no place for her. So her life was a failure. She played the game so long she could not change.

As I have said, parents can err in encouraging the sort of games that cause trouble later. A little boy dressed like a gangster shoots his father, mother, friends, brothers, sisters, and playmates for a long time before he has the nerve to shoot for real. It is so easy to kill with a stick gun, with mother's dishcloth over his face. When the real thing comes, the shooting is not hard for he has been laughed at as he committed the make-believe crime over and over again. Parents and playmates played dead for him and it was great fun. But when the gun he fires or the knife he stabs with is not made of wood or rubber and the victim does not get up laughing, the story is not so good. His life has been ruined. The games he has played as a child have swallowed him up in sin and disgrace.

I would not say that a little boy should not have a cowboy suit or a gangster outfit. But this must come at the right time in a child's life for him to learn. When the boy wants and gets the cowboy suit, this is the time and the opportunity to teach him the truth about cowboys and also what it means for people to kill and rob. The time to teach a child a lesson is when he is interested. If parents are ready to help the child to see the good or bad in these interests as they appear, teaching is easy. If we are not interested, learning is hard; therefore, we have to watch each interest the child shows and at that time make it simple and very plain to him what that act would mean to the child or to other people. A little boy will say, "I am going to kill my dog." Now is the time to say, "Tomorrow you won't have him. Poor little dog! He wants to live, run, and play like Lassie. If you kill him, you will not have a dog; and it hurts so bad to be killed. You would not want to be hurt like that, and a good little boy would not hurt a sweet little dog like Fido. Killing is bad."

We have to watch for the opportunity to break down the bad things a child has learned from the movies and television about cowboys and what cowboy clothes and guns suggest. Generally, cowboys were not a bad lot, and they were not killers. Parents have their best opportunity to teach their children about what it means to kill when the children have their faces covered with gangster masks or are dressed in their first cowboy suits. This teaching must start young, and the child's desire to kill and rob must be counteracted by teaching him properly day after day. Precept after precept, line after line, is a parent's God-given opportunity to do something worthwhile on this earth. Clothes bring up the subject; then that gives the parent the proper opportunity to teach.

We start playing life early and it is important that our play be directed, that parents should not encourage, make pleasant, or a lot of fun a game that will not bring happiness when it becomes a part of their child's actual life. We see children dress themselves and play out the role of doctor, nurse, school teacher, mama, papa, preacher, farmer, banker, lawyer, and many, many more ways of life, good or bad. They continue to play until it is real.

When children are old enough to go to school, parents should dress them in neat and clean clothes, with haircuts in keeping with the times. When a child is sent to school dressed too much better than his friends, he will be unhappy. The same is true of dressing a child with clothes that are not neat and clean. No matter how poor or how rich a child is, he is conscious about his clothes and his behavior in school depends a lot on the way he is dressed. Over-dressing will cause as much trouble as under-dressing, and every child has a right to be clean.

In the work I have been doing for the past fifty and more years with neglected children, it is impossible not to see how appearance influences behavior and health. I remember one mother that came in one day with most of her teeth out, dirty, and sad. She had with her two little dirty, ragged girls with sad faces. The story was this: "My husband won't come home any more. He has a girl friend, and he doesn't seem to know he has these two little girls." I looked at her and I thought if her husband were my son, I could not blame him for not coming home. After checking the children and getting a good history on how they lived and why they were in such bad shape, I decided not to give them clothes and food that day but to see what that family could do with what they had. I said, "Mother, I want you to try this little experiment for one month. Take the money you spend for tobacco and buy soap and starch and pay on getting your teeth corrected. Wash these children and yourself once a day. Curl their hair and yours. Wash, starch, and iron the clothes you and the children wear. Cook and serve food on a table set up three times a day. If you don't have a cloth for the table, use paper, but make it neat. Have a word of thanks to God for the food you have. Have a bed time for these little girls, and be sure they are in bed early so you will have some time for your husband. Do this for one month and come back."

One month later they were back, clean, neat, and happy. The father came this time, and the mother said, "Papa has completely changed. He has a wonderful time with the girls and he never stays out any more." It was not money they needed. They needed to be lovable so they could be loved. A clean, neat dress, along with a neat hair-do, is a great tonic. I have often thought that our charity clinic would do more good if we had a barber, bath tubs, laundry, tooth brushes, and sweet powder than it does with medicine.

At about twelve or thirteen years of age boys and girls should have been trained in the art of dressing to the extent that it should not be a problem. But with many outside influences such as movies, televi-sion, clothing advertisements, and all kinds of books and magazines, the young people are so confused that they don't know what to do. Many of these outside influences teach them that the only way to attract the opposite sex is by exposing their bodies in a way that will gain attention. So girls think they must dress to have sex appeal. Listening to the day to day discussion on the subject one would think that this sex appeal idea is modern, but it is as old as the human race. Women, from the beginning of time, have used this method of attracting men. It does work, and men fall for it, but in the end no man ever feels kindly toward a woman who has won him that way. She is always that type of woman to him, and he can never feel quite sure she may not use this method on someone else. There is nothing so beautiful as the body of a normal, healthy teenage girl, but a man does not want to share that beauty with other men. He wants it all for himself. And he never completely trusts a girl who dresses in a manner that indicates she is not saving this sacred privilege for her own husband.

Herod was overcome with Salome. He promised her anything in his kingdom, but I am sure he had no respect for her and that when he came to himself, he hated her and also himself. Uriah's wife knew that David walked on his roof every evening, and she was sure that her beauty would attract even a man as strong as David. And it worked. The devil knows how to catch a man, and he has given that secret to woman. With her beautiful body adorned to reveal, a man has a poor chance.

We must teach our children how to dress. We must teach our daughters that to be beautiful is a gift of God, but to be vulgar is destruction. A girl should be taught that the body should be dressed as beautifully as possible, but she must not accentuate the parts that would tempt a man beyond his self-control. For instance, a girl is invited to a ball. She wears a dress that shows a great portion of her bosom. A decent boy will not feel free to look at her all evening, for he will think that she thinks he is looking where he has no right to see. A dress too revealing has spoiled many evenings for a young man and the girl he loves for there is always a feeling of embarrassment that destroys the freedom that makes a perfect date.

The same is true with dresses that fit too tightly or are too thin or with shorts that are too short. For a girl to go on an outing with shorts too short or too tight is always embarrassing to the young man who takes her, for there cannot be that carefree attitude which makes an outing a success if the boy is handicapped by the exposure of her body. I am sure some girls are innocent about such matters and that they never know why they do not have as much fun as the girl dressed in the proper clothes. Any form of pants that fit too tightly detracts from a girl's chances to win the man who would love and respect her. No matter how much a woman would like to change her sex, she has to remain a woman, and the more she tries to dress like a man and act like a man, the farther she drives a real man away. Man, no matter how low he goes or how high he goes, always likes to say, "I have the finest mother on earth." He would like to say the same about his wife, and the way she dresses has much to do with his judgment of how good or how bad she is.

There should be volumes written about the effect of clothes on the behavior of the human race. Take a look at a beautiful girl in a pair of old dirty, tight Levis, her hair unkempt and a cigarette in her mouth! Nobody would ever expect that girl to be some day the mother of a great doctor, lawyer, or preacher. Or observe a young expectant mother at the shopping center with legs and feet bare, dressed in tight pants, smoking, skin yellow and "cobblestoned," teeth stained, hair dry and unruly! Would a decent man want that woman to be his wife, or would he want her to be the mother of his children or his grandchildren? We owe it to our children to dress in such a manner that they will not be ashamed of us. We must teach our children to dress in such a manner we would not be ashamed of them.

We talk about "this modern age," and we assume that being "modern" is something new. But it is not; it is as old as the human race. Each younger generation pursues that which is "modern" . . . whether it be styles in clothing, manners, or entertainment. It is the task of the older generation to try to save the younger generation as much heartache as possible by putting what is "modern" in its proper perspective. Many times human life is simply wasted because a young person, without knowing any better, reaches out for what he considers "new and modern."

Thousands of little children are brought into the world who are consumed by the world and never seem to get anything out of life or leave anything to posterity except embarrassment and shame. Just here today, in the dives tomorrow, and then gone. Some leave children who try to forget their parents, but cannot. Then these children go through life with the picture of a mother or father that will haunt them as long as they live, and their children can never be proud of their grandparents. Life is just one day, and it is over. Why can't parents be an example for their children to model themselves after?

A child without a goal or something to live up to is like a frightened rat in a globe. Every child should have a chance, and every child should have parents who are worthy of the sacred right of rearing another soul who must in time walk alone.

Boys and men have never been as careless with their dress as girls and women. Every man should dress himself in such a manner as to make his sons and daughters proud of him. To see a father going around with his body naked to the waist is not a beautiful sight. I am sure no wife or daughter could consider such a man attractive nor would she be proud to have her friends drop in and see him dressed that way. A well-dressed man is always handsome, but a man with a bare chest or with shorts that are too short is not very attractive.

Two-year-old boys or girls know that the body should be covered and should not be looked on as public property. They refuse to have their clothes off before the opposite sex or the same sex outside the family. No matter how hard man tries, he cannot destroy this inborn knowledge that the body is a sacred object and is not for public display. Clothing styles try to change this awareness but there is still in every living soul that feeling of shame when he displays this sacred gift. Clothes play such a big part in man's behavior that proper dress should be one of the major teaching problems of every mother and father from the day a child is born until he is grown. When we meet a person, the way he is dressed makes us pass judgment on him. You may say that this is wrong, and I am sure that it is wrong many times, but man has done this since the beginning of time.

Some time ago there was much excitement in the Atlanta papers about a boy in a small Georgia town who wanted to go to school with a long duck-tail haircut. The teacher sent him home and said he could not come back to school until he had his hair cut. There were many letters to the editors saying, "This is a free country, and a teacher has no right to send a boy home because he wants to dress a certain way." That statement sounds good, but if we will think this through, we will see that the teacher was right. The father took the case to court but did not win. A good teacher knows that his job is to prepare boys and girls to get the most out of life. He knows that teaching the three R's is a very small part of what he must do to help develop these young people so they can never say, "I was rejected because my teacher never taught me the value of the appearance of my body and of good manners." This particular boy may have had a

good scholastic record, but knowledge without wisdom is like a ship
without a sail. It is not good.

We must teach our children the truth about freedom. This is a free
country, we say, but freedom without wisdom is dangerous. A child
cannot be free until he learns that his freedom must not destroy his
life or that of any other person. Freedom to dress as we like has
caused more trouble than we could imagine: men passing judgment
on women, children passing judgment on mothers, teacher passing
judgment on pupil, man passing judgment on man, woman on
woman. The old adage "what you are speaks so loudly I can't hear
what you say," may be rephrased into "what you look like is so evident I can't see what you are."

The way our children go dressed to school is just as important as
the subjects they learn. The average person is in school twelve to
sixteen years and, whether or not he is taught by his parents the
value of personal appearance, if the school would do its duty, many
of these young people who fall by the wayside could be saved. I
occasionally go to a class of medical students. Some of them come
into class with a cup of coffee in one hand and a cigarette in the
other, shoes unpolished, and often clothes that are not neat. These
men and women are going out to teach people how to get the most
out of life, and they should set an example. I am sure more doctors
have failed by their personal appearance than by their lack of knowledge in this great job of giving people health and happiness.

The girl who goes to school with a pretty hairdo and a neat, clean
dress can learn better than a girl who wears clothes that are revealing, soiled, masculine, or not in keeping with what one would consider the normal dress for a schoolgirl. The little girl whose clothes
are modest, clean, and neat may not think of her attire at all and she
will feel free and happy with the class. The child whose attire is out
of line is always conscious of her appearance even though she may
wear these clothes for sex appeal or to show that she is "casual" and
that she can run her own life and will not be bothered with what is
"conventional." To see a beautiful girl dressed like a woman of the
world, or a handsome boy dressed like a gangster is one of the saddest sights in the world, for we know that in that young person's
body is a soul. Some mother watched over that child night after
night and day after day, dreaming about what this boy or girl would
do to make a better world. Then she sees all these dreams and all the
hours of hard work produce a person who used his freedom to de-

stroy his chances in the world. Death is not half so bad because the parents have to live on with the constant reminder that their child has completely wasted away the life they have created.

A grandmother came to my office one day with a little boy. He was thin and sick and had a very sad face. I said to her, "What is your trouble?" She said, "Doctor, this is my little grandson. His mother was a fine girl and wanted to give her life to help other people. We sent her to college and tried to give her every chance to develop the life we had created for her. She got married and had this child. They got rich quick. She started drinking and all the other things that go with it, and soon she and her husband were separated. She left this child with me, and I have no idea where she is. I am old and sick, but I will do my best with this child if you will help me to get him in good health and tell me how to rear him. I have made a complete failure with my daughter."

After I checked the child and made an outline for his care, I said to the grandmother, "This little boy can be a great blessing to you and you will be a blessing to him. He is neat, clean and well mannered. He will love you and you will find that you can love your daughter more through him. You tell me you did your best for your daughter even though her father was an alcoholic, and I am sure you did. But you must remember that when a human being is born, there are two forces in him: one for good, one for evil. No matter how well we train our children and plan for their lives, when they get old enough to think, they have to decide between good and bad, and we cannot do that for them. It is sad to see your life's work torn to bits by the devil, but each human being has to make his own decisions as to whether he takes God or the devil. All human conflicts go back to this constant fight in a human body as to which force will live in this body, the home of the soul. Your daughter decided for the wrong side.

"Now that you have done your best to give her a constructive way of life, you must believe as I tell you that the devil has persuaded your daughter that his way is the best. But you can't give up. You must give this little boy a chance and teach him each day that he too will have to decide which road he will travel no matter how much you do for him. If parents could make this decision for their children, there would never be another broken heart. Because no matter what a man does in this world, he never wants his children to do wrong and have a hard time."

Day after day parents should set the right example for their children, at the same time impressing on them that their way of life has to be their own selection. If a child has been dressed right, taught right, and the parents have been a living example of right, the decision he makes is likely to be for good and not for evil. He knows what is right and what it has meant to his parents. If the "I do as I please" life seems more attractive, he may try it and find that his parents were right and he may come back and make a good parent and a good citizen. If a child has not been properly trained, it is harder for him to see the value of a human body and the value of making a better world, a world they who trained him have never known.

Again I say we must teach our children that the minute we meet a person, that person cannot help passing judgment on us. The first impression of a person is made on how he or she is dressed and, unless this person has been taught the importance of being properly dressed, he may be judged wrong. This happens every day in the business world as well as in the social world. When a girl or boy goes out looking for a job, the thing that counts most when he walks in is not the number of references he may have but the way he looks. When we meet a person for the first time, we size him up in one glance. Maybe this is wrong, but all human beings are made that way. We may be clever and cover up our feelings toward the person we meet, but until he proves he is not what he looks like, this judgment stands and that first impression is hard to forget. If we are to get the most out of life, we must present ourselves in the way we would like to be judged.

We may say, "What does it matter how I dress at home before my children?" Children are passing judgment on us just the way we pass judgment on other people. Our little son and daughter would like to remember their parents as the perfect mother and father, parents they can be proud to show off. A woman may dress up for a guest, but for her children and husband she may decide that anything will do. Which is most important—our children's and husband's judgment or what our guests will think?

The body is the temple of the soul, and it should be adorned as the most beautiful temple on earth so our children can use it as an example and a model to build upon. A great builder would not start a house without a model, and children must have a model. This model should be the parents, the teacher, the doctor, the minister, as well as all grownups. Children should be taught as they grow to take all these models and use them to build for themselves the kind of temple they would like best to live in. Every day we hear this statement: "I surely would like to be like that person." Would we be willing to do what that person had to do to be that person? No, it was easier to neglect our clothes and our body and our education. We don't want to be any better than we are; if we did, we would. I see mothers with dirty, pot-bellied, poorly clad children who say, "I would give anything to get this little fellow in good shape." But if she really wanted to do any better, she would. We do in life what we want to do. We say we want a thing, but we want someone to give it to us. We are not willing to pay the price. Let us teach our children that "life is real and life is earnest and the grave is not its goal," and that this little house we are living in is just as beautiful as we make it; and it should be kept as a temple of God.

♂ ♀

6. Nursery school and kindergarten

There are women who have to leave their children and go out to work for food and a place to live, but the State would save money and tragedy if it would close up the nursery schools and kindergartens in which they leave the children and finance the mothers so they could stay home and keep their own children and give them a mother's training. One may say that many women are not capable or don't want to be bothered with this job, and unfortunately there are a good many of this type in our country today. We read in the magazines and papers articles about woman's rights and how she should not be tied down in a home with a husband and children to look after when she has the education and the mental ability to do great things instead of spending her life doing a job a maid could do just as well.

Then the great and profound question comes up. Is a life spent making a better gadget greater and more important than a life spent making a child into a man or woman? This question should be discussed before a couple gets married and again before a child is born. No woman who really thinks this question through and who truly loves her child and husband would give up by choice the job of making her child into an adult in order to go out and work for some other man or woman or somebody else's child. To work for somebody you love above all other people on earth should be the height of every person's ambition. Every child deserves a mama and a papa, and if both leave him, he is surely handicapped.

Surely woman has a right to do as she pleases in the United States today, but if she does not have the desire to love and train the child she brings into the world, she should not have the child. She can keep from having children in two ways: First, by not getting married to a man who wants a home and children and thus spoil his life and bring into the world children that know and feel they are not wanted. The unwanted children are one of the doctor's big problems. A mother with a guilt complex about her unwanted child is always overly anxious and indulgent, and the child can never feel secure. Second, she should not get married at all, or she should marry a man who does not want children or a home.

This is an era that will go down in history as a time when children were the most neglected in true mother care and home ties and the most indulged in gifts and money to soothe the parents' consciences; a period when children were the least trained by their own parents. The mother who neglects her child is hard to deal with when the child gets sick or hurt.

The nursery and kindergarten people are making a place for these unfortunate children, but there is no substitute for a mother.

This is an example of the way thousands of little children are treated today by mothers who think homemaking is menial. Mama and papa, up at six o'clock, must get the children up and bathed in a hurry, must get breakfast, and be at the office or other place of business by eight-thirty. They get up unhappy because they did not get enough sleep. Breakfast is rushed and forced on the children who will not eat fast or maybe not at all. Time is passing fast, and they must get to work; papa and mama get mad, talk loud, blame each other for not getting the children to eat. The children are too upset to eat or use the bathroom. At seven-thirty the station wagon arrives, and the children are rushed off without breakfast or a good elimination.

Mama and papa rush off to their separate jobs. Mama works for a handsome man who seems to always be in a good humor; his clothes are neat, and she becomes dissatisfied as she compares her husband with the man she works for. This man she works for has a good wife at home who looks after his children and his clothes and has time to see that he has good food served well. He feels that the money he makes is spent for a good cause and he is a happy man. The man she is married to could be happy if he had a wife who would make a home for him even though they would not be able to buy as many gadgets as they can buy with both working. Occasionally the woman actually falls in love with the handsome boss because he seems so perfect but if she were the boss's wife, he would not be that perfect. A dissatisfied man is not a good person to work for or live with, and a good wife is the best tonic to make a happy man. The working woman who falls in love with the boss will find him to be just like the one she is married to after she becomes his wife.

Papa rushes out and to the office and he may become attracted to a beautiful girl working for him. She has attractive clothes, pretty hands; she has no children or home to keep, no clothes to wash, pots to scrub, dishes to do. So he may compare his wife who is trying to carry two full-time jobs with this girl who works for him. She is happy and not too tired, has all the money she makes to buy clothes, has money to take trips and broaden her topics of conversation. She has time to read and keep up with the times, she is entertaining to be with, and it might put papa to thinking, "If I were married to a girl like that, I would be happy." But that girl would be just like the tired wife he has if she had him and his children and held down a full-time job away from home.

Both mama and papa spend a day at hard work they are being paid to do, and they may be unhappy because they are comparing the people they work with to the people they live with.

Little Johnny has been in nursery school all day among people with whom he would not dare be his normal self, for no child will act for anybody except his own mother or father. The teacher will say, "Mrs. Jones, Johnny is the best little boy I ever had." But when mama and papa show up, he starts whining and showing his temper. Johnny's routine at nursery runs like this. He gets there at seven-thirty to eight; at ten o'clock morning snack. (He did eat a few mouthfuls of food at breakfast.) Lunch at twelve o'clock which he eats because he is afraid not to eat, and there is not present anybody he loves to whom he can voice his objection to food. So he eats it all. Nap time at two o'clock, sleeps two hours, up at four, has a glass of milk and some cookies. At six o'clock, back in the station wagon and taken home.

Mama and papa have just arrived, papa tired and remembering how kind and nice the office girl had been to him and how good she looked when she left the office; mama tired and conscience stricken about her neglected child, but remembering how kind the boss talked and how patient he was. Johnny was fed four times during the day and since his stomach did not have a chance to empty, he has the stomach ache from constant eating, and he is not hungry. He has slept all afternoon and is not sleepy.

Now supper has to be fixed, clothes to wash and iron for tomorrow, baths to get, apartment to clean as they did not have time to clean the apartment or wash dishes before going to work. Now mama says to papa, "I'm just as tired as you are, I have worked all day in the office, so put that paper down and give Johnny his bath while I cook supper." Johnny objects. He has not had a chance all day to show his will power, for he could not do this to a person who is not a good audience. So the show starts. Johnny will not take off his clothes. Papa tries first to persuade, then to bribe, then to tease. When all that fails, he uses a loud voice and then the belt. That makes mama mad so she comes in and finishes up the bath, and the little fellow finds out he doesn't have to mind papa when mama is around.

Supper is on the table, and it is a job to get Johnny in his chair. He had food just two hours ago, and his stomach is full of food that cannot leave until it has been digested. Papa serves his plate, and Johnny pushes it back and says, "I don't want to eat." Mama tries a little game to get him to eat, but he is not hungry. Papa tries to feed him and both mama and papa try all the tricks in the book to get him to eat, but it does not work. Then they speak in cross tones to each other, and Johnny is spanked and put down. Mama and papa don't talk any more until they have swallowed what food they have on their plates,

They would like to get Johnny to bed, for the house work would be much easier if he were out of the way and not turning over chairs, turning up the television too loud, jumping off the best sofa, slamming the doors, and putting in a good amount of crying. All this he does to get attention and to show papa that he can't do much about his conduct while mama is around. (If the child is a girl, she shows mama up for papa will be sorry for her.) Mama is conscience stricken about poor Johnny because she knows she is neglecting him, and she cannot stand to see him spanked by his father. She knows she needs the spanking herself.

So they try to get Johnny to bed. He is not sleepy, for he has slept all afternoon (although no child needs a nap in the daytime after he is two years old). He is undressed by force and put to bed but he will not stay, calls for water time and again, then eventually just crawls out. They give up and let him have his way until they get all the work done, which is about eleven-thirty. So they all go to bed and sleep for six hours provided Johnny will quit calling out, "Mama, don't leave me; Mama, I don't want to go to sleep."

This is the life thousands of little children are living in this country today. How could we expect anything good out of children brought up like this? A child is like any other animal—the mother must train him until he is ready to get out and think for himself. There are thousands of questions that must or should be answered by mama and papa, questions a child would not ask anybody else. These questions they ask over and over, and the parents should answer in simple terms at first and gradually more technical terms until the child learns this special family's way of life. He learns to be a Jones or a Smith. He learns to talk, walk, sleep, eat, behave like a Jones or Smith. I hear this so often, "Doctor, this child just doesn't do at all like I did when I was a child." That is so true. He has been trained by someone else and he acts like his trainer. This training is so gradual that we cannot see what we are doing to our children but if one will listen to a little three-or four-year-old boy or girl at play, he will learn much about himself that he does not realize he is passing on to his child.

My child always played under my office window (my office was in our home). When I was examining a child, I could hear her and it was very revealing to listen as she played out the role of my conduct in the home. Sometimes I could see where I could improve my way of life. She would use the same phrases to her doll that I had used to her, the same form of discipline, and the same methods I carried out in the home. I learned much listening to her play.

No minute of the day from birth to six years can be wasted if we are to develop a well-adjusted child. He is in constant motion all of his waking hours. There is a stubbed toe, a bumped head, a skinned knee, a broken doll, a torn dress, a lost toy, a glass of milk on the floor, a bumped nose, and, if more than one child, there may be a few good fights. These mishaps not only need medical care, but the child must be taught by each of these experiences that the thing he did to get hurt was his own fault and how he can avoid this mishap next time and how he has to pay for every transgression,

We should teach the child that when he gets hurt, it may be his fault and that he is not always being mistreated as so many children are taught. If the dog snaps him or the cat scratches him because he pulled their tails, the cat and dog get the punishment and he is taught that they were at fault. This should never be done, but the child should be punished for hurting the pets. This is the most wonderful way to teach a child that he cannot run roughshod over everything or everybody without having to suffer for it.

Each day as a little child follows his mother while she does her work, he learns a little more until he soon wants to help with the dishes and other chores. Now when this time comes and he drops his mother's choice cup, she should not raise her voice or punish him, but tell him that was mama's best cup, and now it is gone, and we can't have it any more. She should tell him when he helps her, to hold things tight so they will not drop. He learns a lesson and will not be discouraged in his efforts to learn. If this same little boy picked up a cup in a temper and threw it across the room, the good old tried-and-proven method of discipline should be used. A little switch to the legs is the best method and his mother should not say she is sorry she switched him for then he will know she was wrong. This matter of rearing children is the most tedious, demanding job on earth and there is no substitute for a mother.

Some children are forced into foster homes and nursery school or kindergarten and these people are doing a good job in many cases; but they should be taught more about anatomy, digestion, and discipline if they are to make reasonably normal people out of the unfortunate children. Ordinarily their discipline problem is not too great with children from two to six if they are mentally normal, for children at this age will act only for the people they love, who make a good audience for their show. With no mother or father to act for or to show up as a conquered subject, the nursery school has very little trouble with discipline. The great harm resulting from the nursery school is that the child is not privileged to live with the mother during his negative period when he will say "no" to a two hundred pound papa or mama and stick to it even if it costs him a spanking or will let meal after meal go by without taking food to show his strength. He can't learn these lessons that he is a subject instead of a king except with his parents.

The eating habits developed in the nursery school are not at all normal. I have never been able to figure out why the nursery school and kindergarten people want to feed children between meals. They are handicapped enough not having a mother to train them, without having their physical bodies made less efficient by constant eating and afternoon sleeping. These indulgences add up to night spanking, poor health, anemia, poor eating habits, and late bedtime. All this eating between meals makes more work for the kindergarten and nursery school, increases the cost and destroys the child.

Then as to the afternoon nap, all the research that has been done on sleep shows that afternoon naps make poor night sleepers. These little children don't need a nap at all and, if they don't have it, they will be ready for bed at bedtime and will not have to be spanked, causing mama and papa to have words and letting the child find out just how much temper mama and papa really have. We could save many marriages and homes for these parents who have to work out all day and then have to keep a home, if we would send little Johnny home from the nursery school hungry and sleepy so he would be ready to eat and sleep. Then the other work could be done and mama and papa could have a quiet time together and an opportunity to read or talk. These nursery schools and kindergartens could be a great blessing to the child who has no mother, or a mother who has to work, or a mother who doesn't want a child, or a mother who thinks the outside job is more important than building a child, if they would work out a good mother's schedule with them.

A mother in the home is not in the yard with her child all the time. That is where children learn to live with each other and work out their own problems. Supervised play is good if we are trying to teach the art of some game, but the child learns to live by the way he plays and a child will not play normally before adults. In his play he is educated for good or bad by the children with whom he plays. I hear the statement of a mother so often in my office, "I don't know what I am going to do with my son, for he just can't get along with children. Every time he goes out they start picking on him and he comes in crying." When I ask her what she does, she says, "Then I go out and send the children home." I remind her that this little boy will not have her available to go out and send people home all his life and that he must work this out himself. When he comes in crying and says, "They hit me, or they won't play with me," she should just say, "Son, if they don't play like you want to play and you children can't get along together, don't go out." When he finds out that she is not going out to fight his battles for him, he will make a greater effort to get along and will soon be having a good time. Children, the same as adults, will love and respect any child who will play fair or fight fair and will not try to hide behind his mother's skirt, show-ing the children that his mother will not let them do back to him as he has done to them, and that he can hit and run to her for protection. A mother should always console a child who has been hurt physically or mentally but never console a child, even though he is hurt, if he is in.the wrong.

The normal home type of play should be simulated in the nursery school and kindergarten as nearly as possible.

Every day in a child's life counts, but none like the years from birth to six. If a child has been away from home in nursery or kindergarten, there is no thrill when he is six and it is time to start to school. He has been in a so-called school and it has been all play. He has had the teacher and he has had the children, and there is nothing in regular school to thrill him. All of this feeling of a change in his life and the feeling of growing up and getting away from mama is old and I find that it gives rise to big problems. Often the mothers will say, "Doctor, my child will not take any interest in school; he just wants to play like he did in kindergarten, and he does not take the teacher seriously."

Many parents are disturbed about their children when they start school. School should be a privilege, a new experience, and it should be talked about as a great coming event that the children will be certain to enjoy. They can't get this thrill if they have been away from home under the supervision of teachers all their lives. These parents go to the psychiatrist or the pediatrician and say, "Doctor, I have missed the road somewhere. I am lost. I don't know how to get back on the right road with my child." The doctor can help the mother to see where she missed the road, but if parents watch every sign every day, they will not get off the road. I say nobody but the parent can do the job as it should be done; and in the development of a child there is no way to go back and start over.

Each period of development is different and once that period is gone, the training the child should have had at that time and didn't get cannot be given. Children must be guided and they must be inhibited, and they must learn this lesson while they can take it. When we inhibit a child from two to six, he may cry and have a temper tantrum, but he learns that lesson and in a few minutes will be happy and love us. If this happened to an adult, it would not be so easy unless he learned about being inhibited as a child.

Somebody might suggest that laws should be passed to make mothers look after their children. I say that would be the worst thing that could happen. You can't fool a child and if a mother were forced to stay with a child she didn't want to stay with, the child would know it, and the reaction would be worse than the nursery or foster home. When a child has a mother who goes out to work because she thinks the job brings her more honor and happiness than rearing a child, this mother will not let a day go by that she does not bring the child something. This child is not fooled, for he knows his mother is trying to buy his love with things, and he knows this gift comes because she knows she is neglecting him. He would be much happier if she would help him make a toy with some spools or a box. You can't buy a child's love any more than you can buy a wife's or husband's love.

Children learn about love when they see their parents deprive them of something they want that would not be good for them and punish them when they do wrong. These things show that a parent is really interested and that the parent loves the child enough to hurt him if it can make life better for him. If a child is given things to hush him up, he knows it and knows that his parents are not interested in making a good life for him, but their interest is to hush him up so they will not be bothered. This is not a good feeling for one to have. If a husband said to his wife, "Take this money and go to a show," it would not be very flattering and she could not attach much love or interest to the gesture, but if he said, "Come, let's go to the show," or, "We can't afford a show," the situation would be different.

In the nursery school we must try our best to simulate the normal discipline and normal feeding in the home. The average child of today has a cabinet full of toys he never plays with at all, toys that were bought to show him how much he was loved by a parent who did not have any time for him. The little boys or girls who have parents who have time to make a doll dress or a doll, or time to saw some wheels off a log to make a wagon, or take an orange crate and show them how they can make a playhouse, post office or hospital, and create all the equipment out of things they make, are the happy children as well as the children that help with the house work, that help save money, help pack boxes for the less fortunate, help make a present for Grandma . . . children who learn the art of giving.

This job of rearing children presents a thrill every day if we accept it as the most important job on earth, and the one that brings the most happiness to a parent. We must let the child make some mistakes and have to pay for them, or let him make some big deals and see them fail. I remember how my child at four years decided to get rich quick. She fixed up a box on the front lawn, had our wonderful old cook make her a big pitcher of lemonade, got some cups out, took a chair and sat in the hot sun waiting for someone to come along and buy, but nobody came. I kept watching and hoping someone would come by and buy just one cup, but no one did. I felt the urge to go out and buy it all myself. She stayed out there a long time, then gathered up her equipment and came in. I did not say a word, for I knew she had many disappointments ahead of her and this was a good lesson to teach her how to meet the big ones to come. If I had bought the lemonade, she would have lost respect for me because she would have known I was doing it because I did not want to see her disappointed, and that I did not want the lemonade. It is hard to sit by and see a child disappointed, but the earlier children learn they can't have everything they think they want, the better it is. These lessons can be taught best by the child's parents.

When a child is trained from birth to six, he will be a "chip off the old block." A Jones will be a Jones and a Smith a Smith and the child will not be like the kindergarten teacher, the nursery teacher, the maid, or the foster mother.

Every child deserves a chance but I know from more than fifty years of working with children that there are thousands who have never had a decent chance in life. I don't mean a chance at wealth and the things money can buy, but the blessing of a good mother who loves the child and realizes that the march of life is always forward and the opportunity missed today is gone forever. If mothers could only see what they are doing to their children to make them develop a rejection complex by sending them out of the home before they are ready to go, (no child is ready to go before he or she is six years old—and in some cases, older) surely they would make greater effort to avoid it.

The statement I hear over and over again, is "Doctor, my child is getting to be too much of a mama's boy and will not let me get out of his sight." The child knows mama is rejecting him, so he clings closer and closer and cries out at night dreaming he is left out or deserted. I have never heard this statement from a good mother, and I have never seen a child with a rejection complex who was not really being rejected. Another statement I hear often is, "Doctor, there are no children in our block; and I just had to send him off so he could learn how to play with other children, and get him out of my hair." Oh, how these mothers think up excuses to put the training job on somebody else when they don't want the job! We hear the statement again and again, "No mother should be tied down with a house full of kids." No woman who really wants to be a mother is ever "tied down with kids" and the only mother who is "tied down" is the mother who wants to get away. A real mother never has the feeling that she is being punished by having children, but she feels that she has been blessed with the greatest opportunity on earth. Children have to leave home sometime, and six years of age is not too late. We should not push them out of the nest until they are ready to fly. Physically and mentally no child is ready to go before six and some considerably later.

We must have a place for the child who has no mother or the child who has a mother who is forced to work for food and clothes, and we must make this place as much like home as we can in the way children are fed, loved and disciplined.

♂ ♀

7. Looking for the obvious

Parents should be taught to look for the obvious; first in themselves, second in their children.

In this age of specialists our children are taught to accept the fact that we go to a specialist for a solution to all of our problems. A friend of mine called a doctor one night; he had severe pain in his abdomen under the ribs on the right side just to the right of the midline. When the doctor walked in, the man said to the doctor, "I think I am having a gall bladder attack." The doctor said, "Man, you are not supposed to think; leave that to me; I am a specialist and I will make the diagnosis." This doctor made that statement in jest, but it is truly the trend of the day to let someone else do our thinking, someone who just thinks about one thing, and we are taught to accept him as an authority and never question what he says. This is poor training.

A child must be taught to listen but, most important of all, he must be taught to think for himself. Just because Lenin says communism is the perfect way of life does not make it true, and I would regard him as an authority and a specialist on the subject of communism. We should teach our children to question. Some parents get angry when a child asks the question, "Why should I do what you say?" and sometimes this question is answered with a spanking or the reply, "You do what I say because I say so." A child has the right to know why he has to do a thing. Children should be required to do as the parents say, as the parents are their masters and they must learn obedience, but when parents refuse to let their children question, they are starting them off on the wrong road.

Today these children who were taught to let other people do their thinking are the parents who neglect many things about their children that should have been found early. These parents have never been taught to look for the obvious. They say, "We take the baby to the doctor to tell us what to do and to find anything that may be wrong."

Parents must be taught to observe, study, and examine a child from the day he is born until he leaves the home. The doctor may see the baby once a month but the mother and father see him all the time. They can solve many of the little problems that would be big problems before they might see the doctor, or if they see these things that appear abnormal and will bring them up on the next visit to the doctor, they will help the doctor to help the child. "Why does my baby cry so much?" is an everyday question. Has the mother looked at his stools and are they normal? If they are too frequent and watery, there is something wrong with the food or the child is sick. He will not "outgrow" this and he needs help. Maybe he is allergic to the food. Maybe he gets it too frequently and his stomach is over-distended, as frequent feedings cause a delay in emptying time. If the undigested food is passed out with the digested food, diarrhoea may develop. Does the stool have a bad odor? Does the baby have a fever? Maybe the baby has an infection that should be cleared up. Are the stools oily or white? Is the child's abdomen larger than normal? How big are the stools when they are passed? Is the anus as large as the normal anus or does the stool come out as a very small mass? Does the stool come out at the right place? Does the baby cry when he has a stool? Has there been any blood? Does the baby cry when he urinates? If his stools are normal, the abdomen not enlarged, no complaint with the urination, we will have to look for other reasons for the crying. Does the baby take his food well? How about the opening in the nipple? Is the bottle held and pulled back when the baby pulls so he can suck? Is the milk warm? Cold milk delays digestion. Is there a period of four hours between feedings so that the stomach can empty before more milk is added?

Spitting Up

Does the baby spit up? If he does, there is something wrong. We must not believe all babies spit up and that spitting is something to accept. No, if food comes up, there is a reason and that reason should be worked out. If there is a constant return of food from the stomach, the baby soon gets a severe esophagitis from the hydrochloric acid in the gastric juice and this is very painful. The sphincter at the lower end of the esophagus may not be adequate and there is a constant return of food into the esophagus and the mouth and out on the bed. If the spitting is too bad, there may be an obstruction. The food may be too concentrated. The baby could have been injured at birth to cause the spitting. Did the mother smoke while she was pregnant? If so, the baby may spit for several weeks.

Was the mother addicted to any other sedatives or stimulants? Some might say the baby is a ruminator but all the babies that I have seen with this diagnosis cleared up when the formula was made right and the esophagitis was cleared up. The baby seemed to bring up the food to try to stop the burning and pain in the esophagus. There are many other reasons for spitting, but there is always a reason since it is not normal for a baby to spit up food. A mother should study her child and try to find the reason and correct the trouble if she can, but if she can't, she should take all her observations to the doctor and they should work it out together. A baby that spits has to have pressure in the stomach increased enough to bring the food up, and the constant presence of hydrochloric acid in the esophagus causes pain. The pressure in the stomach plus the pain in the esophagus causes him to cry.

Reasons Why a Baby Cries

The baby may cry because he is on his back and he is afraid he is going to fall. When turned over on his abdomen, he will feel secure. The baby may be too hot or too cold; if he is perspiring, he is too hot but if he looks blue, he is too cold.

If the baby stops crying when held on his mother's chest with his head on her warm body, he may have the earache or stomachache. The temperature should be checked and if there is a fever and the reason can't be found, a doctor should be seen at once. If the mother finds the reason for the fever herself, she should do the things she knows to do and if that doesn't help, she should call the doctor.

Maybe there is something in the baby's environment that is causing him to cry and he should be undressed and checked. One mother discovered that she had pinned the diaper pin through the skin. One mother brought in her baby who had cried all day and when I took his socks off, I found a thread wrapped around the big toe. The toe was black and it took several weeks to cure the toe that had been tied off for several hours. If a child cries out at night soon after he goes to bed, the mother should examine the anus area for pinworms. If a child is old enough to handle door knobs and other objects that have been handled by others and the child puts his hands in his mouth, we can be sure he has worms and that will make him cry out at night. Maybe the adults or children frighten the baby while playing with him and he has bad dreams. Television has caused many fears.

There are many reasons why a baby might cry, and parents should look for the obvious and not just believe it is normal for a baby to be unhappy all the time. Parents can do much to find the reason if they will just think and look for the trouble. One mother brought in a little fifteen-months-old girl who was very pale and sick and had been in this condition for several weeks. After removing her clothes, I could see a large mass in her abdomen that was very hard. I asked the mother if she had noticed this big abdomen or felt this huge mass. She said, "No, doctor, but now I can see and feel what you are talking about and I don't know why I did not see this before." This child had a tumor on her kidney which was removed and the child lived, but this child could have been saved weeks of pain if the mother had felt the abdomen or observed the severe anemia.

A mother brings in a child that is so sick and weak he can't sit up. I will ask the mother when she noticed that the child's skin and the whites of his eyes were yellow. She will say, "Doctor, he is as yellow as a pumpkin but I had not noticed it." Then I will ask her the color of his urine and she will say, "I have not looked." "What is the color of his stools?" "I have not looked." She knows he has been sick for three or four days, vomiting and will not eat, has a fever and a stomachache, but that is all she knows. On examination the stools are white, the urine looks like strong tea, the liver is enlarged, there is a fever, and the child looks very sick. Two of the most marked symptoms are his weakness and the yellow color of the skin and eyes. (A mother should always look at the stools a child passes when he is sick—and also check the urine. A child would not be forced to suffer so long if the mother would just look for then she would take the child to the doctor sooner.)

Now this particular child is much sicker than he would have been if he could have been seen earlier. He was treated as follows: one tablespoon of milk of magnesia; two hours later two teaspoons of soda and one quart of water as an enema; then 250 mgs. of aureo-mycin every three hours night and day for ninety-six hours (given by rectum if too sick to keep it by mouth); one cc. vitamin B-complex fortified with vitamin C in the muscle once a day for seven days; no fats; a high protein diet, high sugar, and large amounts of water. This child can be well and out again in ten to fourteen days. If this mother had only looked for the obvious, the treatment could have been started earlier and the amount of damage to the liver from infectious hepatitis decreased.

A mother comes in with a child that has a high fever, has not eaten for three or four days, has bad breath, dripping saliva, cries all the time. I will ask the mother if she had noticed how bad the child's breath was, or if she had seen his red, ulcerated gums and tongue. As a rule she will say, "No Doctor, I did not think to look in his mouth." Just one look in the mouth, or one whiff of his breath, or one look at the constant dripping of saliva should have prompted her to take the child to the doctor three days earlier. The treatment prescribed: 200,000 units of penicillin by mouth every three hours night and day for seventy-two hours; one cc. vitamin B-complex fortified with vitamin C in the muscle once a day for seven days; tincture of mercresin on the gums and tongue once a day for seven days; no milk or milk products. This treatment can cure this type of illness in seven days but as a result of the mother not looking, the disease lasted fourteen days and the child had to be much sicker and had to suffer much longer from Vincent's angina than was necessary.

Upset Stomach and Diarrhoea

A mother will call and say, "Doctor, Mary had a good supper last night. She seemed to feel well and ate more than usual, but about two A.M. she called, and before I could get there, she had vomited and some of the food she brought up was food she had for lunch as well as supper. She has continued to vomit every few minutes since then. Now her stools are watery and frequent, and what she brings up when she vomits is a clear yellow foamy mucus." "What have you done for her?" "Nothing but some kaopectate," "What about water?" "I quit giving water because that seemed to make her vomit more." "Is there any fever?" "No, she feels cold." "Let's try this first and if she is not better in a few hours, or if she develops a fever or any other symptoms, bring her in. First, give her two teaspoons of milk of magnesia. If she vomits that, give two more teaspoons, and if that comes back, don't bother her any more for two hours. Then give her one teaspoon of soda in one pint of water as an enema. To give the enema, place her on her abdomen and run it in very slowly and be sure it all goes in. After the enema, give her one teaspoon of Coca-Cola syrup every fifteen minutes for four doses. After that, start food with nothing but rice, bananas, apple sauce, beef or chicken broth you make yourself with a little more than the normal amount of salt added to the broth, dry toast, jelly, weak hot tea, and all the water she will take. Never hold the water back even though she vomits, for she always absorbs some. Start the broth by giving one teaspoon at a time. Give no other food than that prescribed for four days. Then start one new food a day. It is best to start beef or chicken first, and then add the vegetables and let the milk and citrus fruit be omitted for two weeks."

As a rule, this is all that is necessary to make the child well. If the mother calls back and says Mary has a fever and the stools have a very bad odor, she is brought in and examined. If she has a fever, the stools are thin gray and have a very bad odor, there is acetone in the urine, she is weak, breathing deep and slow, breath with a sweet odor, continues to vomit, and nothing is found on physical examination to account for the sickness, we can be sure she has an intestinal infection. Retention enemas for acidosis are made up and given in this manner: eight ounces of strong tea, twenty-four ounces of water, two tablespoons of dextrose, one-half teaspoon sodium bicarbonate, one-half teaspoon sodium chloride. This mixture is warmed to the temperature of the body and eight ounces is given as a retention enema, and the buttock is held so that it cannot be expelled for at least fifeen minutes. This is given every two hours for four doses.

If the child has the common intestinal infection with fever, this is usually all we have to do. But if the fever and the diarrhoea continue and the vomiting has stopped, chloromycetin or sulfadiazine is started by mouth and the child is kept on the above diet, being sure she does not get milk or milk products for one month. If the temperature becomes normal and the child eats well, but the stools continue to be gray, watery, and have a bad odor, the drug erythromycin has been of great help.

All of these cases should have stool cultures and be studied for protozoa before medication is started, but sometimes this is not possible. We have to do something for the child to save his life and there may not be time to get these tests worked out before the medication is started, and after medication is started, they are of no value. With the dextrose retention enemas we can reduce the acidosis before we have time to get the blood chemistry, and the one and greatest thing to keep in mind is the welfare of the child. If a mother would give her child milk of magnesia and an enema as soon as the vomiting starts and clean out the offending food or organisms that are causing the trouble, she could save the child much unnecessary suffering. If this treatment did not make the child better in a short time, she should call the doctor and not wait until the child developed an acidosis.

There are many reasons why a child will vomit and have frequent stools that cannot be helped by this method, but this treatment can't do any harm. In my practice, I have found it of great help in clearing up a simple sickness before the child developed a major problem. I heard a young doctor laughing one day about the so-called cleaning out doctoring. But he should remember that a child will not vomit or have frequent stools without a reason and nine times out of ten there is something in the intestinal tract that nature is trying to eliminate. A dose of milk of magnesia and a sodium bicarbonate enema can do a great deal to help this condition. Mothers must be taught to do simple things for their sick children while they are waiting for a busy doctor to come.

End Result of Bad Tonsils and Teeth

A mother will call and say, "Johnny has not felt well for several days; he is cross and will not eat, and last night he could hardly walk. After he went to bed, he cried with his right knee." I tell her that I think it would be best for him to see a doctor. The mother brings him in, and I ask her when the child first seemed sick. "Oh, for several months he has had trouble with his tonsils. He will run a fever and I will take him to the doctor who gives him a shot and a tonic. Then he feels better for a few days, but about every two weeks he has a recurrence of the bad throat and fever, but he has not had the pain in his knee until yesterday. He has talked about his legs hurting, but I thought that was because he did not want to go to school. He just will not eat right. I let him sleep as late as he can to get the rest, but he will not eat his breakfast and says the school lunches are not good. They have a milk break at ten o'clock and he has cookies and milk then. When he gets home, I give him milk and cookies trying to make him gain a little weight. He will not eat supper and I feed him milk and cookies before he goes to bed." The boy is checked. His hemoglobin is sixty per cent or less, blood pressure ninety over fifty, pulse eighty-five, white count high, red count low, sedimentation rate increased, color pale, posture poor, muscles soft, temperature one hundred one, cervical glands enlarged, tonsils large and red, heart normal but pulse increased, right knee red, hot, swollen, tender to touch, and he will not move it. He looks like a sick child,

I say to the mother, "This child has acute rheumatic fever, but his heart is not enlarged and there is no murmur at present. What I find today is a child with marked anemia, bad tonsils, and a bad knee. Now to get this boy well we must get rid of the things that are obvious that would make a child sick. First, we will give him 400,000 units of penicillin every three hours night and day by mouth for one week. At the end of the week if the knee is cleared up and the tonsils are not red, we will take him to the hospital and get the tonsils out and continue the penicillin for three more days. Then we will give him sulfadiazine 7.7 gr. three times a day for three weeks. He is to have three meals a day, at seven, twelve-thirty, and six—and no food between meals, no milk or cookies, no drinks except water or lemonade. If he does not want the lemonade, he is to have one hundred mgs. of ascorbic acid with each meal. He should have meat with each meal and vegetables twice a day. Do not talk about food." "Is he to stay in bed?" "No. If the weather is good, keep him out in the open all the time. I don't want him to run and play, but I don't want him in bed. He should come to the table for his food and go to the bathroom.

"This question about staying in bed reminds me of an experience I had some forty-five years ago. When I finished my training in the hospital, I had been well indoctrinated in the theory that a rheumatic fever patient should stay in bed for several weeks or until the temperature was normal and the pulse normal and the heart murmur cleared up. So I had this little girl in the clinic with rheumatic fever and her mother said to me, 'Doctor Denmark, tell Martha she cannot play like other children but she must stay in bed.' The 'in bed' order had been given this child and the mother thought if I gave the order again, the child would understand and stay in bed without so much prodding. When the mother asked me to speak to the child, the child looked up to me and said, 'Doctor Denmark, I would rather play a little and not live so long.'

"Since that day I have never put a rheumatic fever child to bed and I have not lost one. If they are put to bed and away from other children, they soon quit eating, they lose interest, and medicine will not cure them. We must first get rid of the source of the infection (in this case it is the child's tonsils), and then make the child happy and feed him right and keep up his interest. The infection in his tonsils gets better every time he has antibiotics, but just as soon as the antibiotic is gone, the pus in the crypts of the tonsils that harbor hemolytic streptococcus starts the infection over again and soon the heart gets involved. So the bad tonsils must go. If he is put to bed, all his muscles get weak and his heart is no exception. Then when the muscles of the heart are weak and flabby, the heart enlarges and we hear a murmur.

"In treating your child we have to treat the whole child. So we must first get rid of the infection, feed him right, and try to help him build up antibodies against hemolytic streptococcus or any other organisms that will cause a sickness. After three weeks I want him to be started on a mixed vaccine as now available; it is a bacterial combined vaccine with H influenza. He will start with one tenth cc. and increase one tenth cc. twice a week for twelve inoculations, and then he will take boosters for several years, one cc. a month for three inoculations starting in September." "What about his school?" "You should have a teacher come in starting in three weeks and she will help him for one month after which he can go back to school. We must make this little fellow happy and not talk about his bad health."

I remember a little girl I saw my first year of practice. I was taking calls for a doctor who was on vacation, and he had asked me to see this little girl often, for she had rheumatic fever and had been in bed for three months. She continued to run a low-grade temperature each day, was anemic and would not eat, had joint pains and looked sick, and continued to run pus in the urine and a one to two plus albumin in the urine. At that time I was young and smart like most doctors who are just starting out, and would take a chance on what I thought would work. This happened not long after Martha had said, "I would rather play a little and not live so long."

I checked the little six-year-old girl who had been out of school for three months and had not been out of her room or to the table.

She was pale, flabby, thin, and looked sick. Her hemoglobin was low, her white count up, temperature 101 degrees, pus and albumin in the urine, tonsils had been removed. There was no heart murmur, but it seemed a little enlarged and the pulse increased. There were no swollen joints, but all the muscles were soft and flabby, the abdomen was soft, and no abnormal condition found even though she complained of abdominal pain.

She had one tooth that was just a shell, and on the gum just below that tooth was an abscess that drained a large amount of pus when pressed. The tooth was tender to touch. After the examination was finished, I said to the mother, "I want you to take this child to the dentist this very afternoon." The mother looked shocked and said, "Doctor, this child has not been out of bed to go to the bathroom for three months and I would be afraid to take her to a dentist." I said, "She will never be well until you do something about the reason for her sickness and this tooth is one reason." I don't know why she followed my advice but she took the child to the dentist that day and had the tooth pulled. Then I gave these instructions: "Get her out of this room; fix her a cot in the yard and help her to walk out there, give her a sun bath each day. Give her three meals a day with no more in between snacks or drinks, no milk or milk products, all the meat and vegetables she will eat, and the juice of three lemons a day in lemonade following the meals. Take her temperature at six, twelve, and six o'clock. Let her see her friends and play dolls but be sure to keep her out as much as possible, and she can do anything she wants to as to exercise but no running for two weeks."

A week later I saw her again. The temperature had been normal for two days, there was no pus or albumin in the urine, her appetite was good, and she was much happier. In a very short time she was back in school. There were no antibiotics then that we could credit for her improvement, but we had no more symptoms. I am sure this was not a case of rheumatic fever but just bad teeth, too much "in bed," and a milk diet. When our child gets sick, we should do a little looking ourselves, examine the teeth, look at the tonsils, and examine the cervical glands. If they are enlarged, there is an infection above them. Is the child pale, lazy, irritable? Is he being fed properly? We should look for the obvious and save the child before he is sick enough to endanger his health.

A boy was in my office recently who, his mother said, was not doing well in school and would not obey. When she called, he would not come. I examined the boy and he was a fine specimen, but both ear canals were filled with wax and he could not hear. A mother should be able to find this out and get help before the child fails in school or she makes him feel like a nobody. The same is true with respect to a child's interest in what a teacher puts on the blackboard. The teacher should be sure he sees the board before she labels him a bad child. Teachers, parents, and doctors must look for the obvious.

I suspect more harm is done each year to the human race by poor eating habits and the so-called bad colds than any other two things. Mothers are prone to take the bad cold as a matter of course and not do much about it until the child has a high fever or cries all night with the earache. I ask the mother when she noticed the child was sick, and she will say, "Well, he has had a running nose for some time; in fact his nose runs most of the time, but all children have running noses." Mothers must be taught that this thing called a running nose may lead to severe sickness if not cleared up. It is not normal for a child to have pus in his nose, and the pus is not a cold but a bacterial infection. A virus does not cause pus. The cold prepared the child for a bacterial infection or the bacterial infection could have been brought on by an allergic condition in the nose that caused the sinuses to be closed and sinusitis to develop.

In the winter when the child is shut in and the air is filled with tobacco smoke and the mucous membrane swells and the child has a so-called cold, it is not a cold at all but is a sinusitis caused by constant irritation and swelling of the mucous membranes from the smoke which keeps the sinuses closed; and they fill with pus from a secondary infection. Abscessed ears are caused in this manner. I am sure that this one condition causes more earache and sinus trouble than any other one thing today. The same condition can be caused by radiant heaters that are not vented well, or by dust. When a child continues to have a running nose, we should not conclude that this is something every child has and that we needn't bother about it until he has a fever. Children aspirate this pus and develop severe chest trouble; they swallow the pus and will not eat; they sleep with their mouths open and this makes their tongue dry, teeth decay, nose small, and ruins the shape of the face. We should look around to see what we are doing to cause the condition, eliminate smoking in the house, study the heating system, clear away dust, keep the windows open at night, and keep the child out in the open as much as possible.

If he sleeps with his mouth open, a doctor should be seen at once about the adenoids or a possible allergy and if his cervical glands are enlarged, his tonsils should be removed. He should be immunized against pus-forming organisms in this manner: start with one tenth cc. catarrhalis combined vaccine with H influenza, increasing one tenth cc. twice a week for twelve inoculations; it should be given in the arm and in the skin for the first three doses, then as close under the skin as possible. If there is any reaction, the dosage should be cut back but the vaccine continued until the child gets one cc. three times.

When a child is born, he has no immunity or money of his own making, and it takes a lifetime to make his own immunity and his own money . . . and many never make either. With this vaccine, we can help the child to build up antibodies faster and not have to be sick. In August or September for several years following we start with one tenth cc. of the vaccine and build up to six tenths. I have found that these boosters help.

I urge every mother not to be one of the "I don't know anything about children" type who use this statement to cover up rejection and neglect of their child. Recently a mother came in with a little girl eight months old. The mother said, "Doctor, this baby has cried for eight months and we have not had a full night's sleep since we brought her home from the hospital. I tell you, Doctor, I don't know a thing about babies and for eight months this child has had a cold, will not eat, and will not sleep. I am a medical secretary and I have two college degrees. I liked my work and did a good job but at this job of being a mother I have failed."

I said to the mother, "Man is a funny animal. The things he wants to do are never hard, and he never finds obstacles in the path of a real desire. You were happy working with the doctors, you could dress beautifully, and have people tell you how well you were doing your job. This job of being a mother you did not want." "Yes, that is true. With all my education this looks like I am throwing my life away." "What is the most important job on earth?" "I don't know."

"The greatest job on earth is to build a man or woman. Any woman might do the job of a medical secretary but there is only one person on earth who can be a mother to your child. These people who make you feel great in the business world will soon pass on and you will be forgotten, but this child will be what you make her and pass that on to another generation. You could start a trend of neglect that might go on indefinitely. What you are saying in truth is you don't want this job and your baby knows it. Let's change that statement from 'I don't know' to 'I don't want to do.'" The baby was examined; it was pot-bellied, pale, nose running, both ears abscessed. "How do you feed this baby?" "On demand." "How do you sleep this baby?" "On demand." "Do you get her outside?" "No, I don't have time; I don't have time for anything since she came."

A good schedule was worked out: breakfast at seven consisting of eggs, cereal, fruit, meat, and a raw fruit, banana, a cup of water; nap at ten; lunch at twelve-thirty consisting of meat, vegetables, fruit, cereal, cup of water; out in the open until six when she has dinner consisting of the same foods as at lunch; a bath and to bed. Penicillin 200,000 units every three hours night and day for seventy-two hours for the abscessed ears. She was sent home with this statement, "Go home and feel that you are blessed above so many women. You are a queen in your home and you have the greatest job on earth, that of building a human being, and it may be that this little girl you are blessed to have may be the mother of another great human builder. You should do all you can to make her life as perfect as possible." One month later this mother came back and the baby was happy, they had not missed any more sleep, and the mother was so grateful that she had learned the true value of things. Her trouble had been so obvious, but she would not open her eyes to see.

A mother can make her home a heaven or a hell and she alone can make a home. She should look around and see what she is doing to the child she has been blessed to have. The greatest happiness that ever comes to a human being is to see a job well done and the job of rearing a child, if it is well done, brings the most lasting happiness.

We should look for the obvious and save our child. We don't have to be a tyrant, or carry a bull whip, but should be a parent who will take a child by the hand and lead him into a way of life that will prepare him to make a better world. Our child wants a master, not a brother or sister. He wants somebody to look up to, somebody to brag about. He wants somebody to help him over the rough places in life. Somebody to carry him when he cannot make it. Why can't we parents see what we are doing to our children just because we will not look for the obvious?

A mother called and said her child continued to soil his underpants. He will not have a big stool in his pants but will continue to pass something all during the day. She has spanked, bribed, and shamed but it does no good. He will not go to the bathroom and have a stool like he should, but holds back. The child is brought in and on rectal examination a large fecal impaction is noted that has been there for weeks. When I asked the mother when the child had the last formed stool, she said she didn't know as he goes to the bathroom by himself and she doesn't keep up with that.

I had one ten-year-old boy who had been wearing diapers to school for a year. He had been told that his anus was paralyzed and the stools just leaked out. On examination there was found a mass of stool four inches in diameter that was very hard and he could not pass it, so the soft stool passed around this mass. The mass was so large, the anus could not be completely closed and there was a continuous passing of soft stool. This mass of stool was removed manually and the boy was put on a good diet with no milk or milk products and a regular time to go to the bathroom, and he had no more trouble. This is a common occurrence in pediatrics and has resulted in much punishment for children. No child over two years old will soil his pants if he can help it and, when a child continues to have soiled pants, he should have a good examination and the reason found . . . for there is a reason.

Bed Wetting

The same is true with respect to a child wetting his pants or the bed after two years of age. A mother will say her little girl keeps her pants wet and seems to be afraid to urinate. On examination the child is found to be red and very sore in her vulva and when she starts to urinate, it burns so she cuts it off and there is a constant desire to go and a constant fear of burning. If the mother would examine her little girl, she would see why she had wet pants. The child may use the toilet paper wrong, pulling the paper forward and smearing the stool in the vulva, causing an infection; or she may be getting something she is allergic to that causes the rash; or she may be getting too much citrus or tomato which may make the urine alkaline and cause the burning. In some of these cases the labia minora have grown together and the urine has to be forced out of a small opening which causes pain.

A mother should check her child at bath time and if she finds some abnormal condition, she should see a doctor at once as there are many reasons why a child cannot control the urine. Infection, malformation, and small bladders are very common in the urinary tract. A few things we can do to keep these little girls from getting in trouble are: teach them how to use the toilet paper, keep them clean, give them no drinks except water. If there is trouble after these three simple things have been done, then the child should see a doctor. Girls don't want to be wet.

The same is true with respect to boys. They should be examined and kept clean and not allowed to drink all kinds of sweet drinks, carbonated water, too much milk, or enough citrus to cause an alkaline urine. Diapers should not be used after two years. There is always a reason for wet beds and wet pants after two years and parents may be responsible for much of this because they permit the child to drink all day things he should not have, and never examine him to see if he is irritated or cannot stand to empty his bladder. A schedule of three meals a day and no drinks except water has saved many of my little patients.

Last winter a mother with seven children called me and said, "My sister who lives in Ohio is sick in bed. She has three children and cannot care for them. I am the only person to take the children and her. They have no money to pay for help. The father works, but he can do no more than buy food." I asked her the trouble. She said, "She just can't get out of bed as her body is in so much pain. She won't eat and the doctors can't find the trouble." I suggested that she bring her to Atlanta and see what the doctors here could find.

She was examined by every test and X-ray, and they could not find any reason why she could not do her work and stay out of bed. So this mother called again and said, "My sister is no better and it is believed that she needs psychiatric help." I asked if her teeth were examined. She said, "No, but you should see her teeth; she has gum boils and all her teeth are full of cavities." "Did they examine her tonsils?" "I am sure they did, but she has had trouble with her tonsils since she was a child and she has big glands in her neck." I said, "Let's do two more things before we call in a psychiatrist. Take her to my dentist and to an otolaryngologist." She went to the dentist and the throat doctor. The dentist said he had never seen worse abscesses in teeth. The teeth which he could not fix were pulled, and the tonsils were removed. In two months this mother was back home doing her work. We doctors are guilty at times of not looking for the obvious. We like to look for things hard to find and we miss the killers.

A well-educated couple came into my office with a beautiful well baby that I had been seeing from birth. They were all worried about the baby because I had not checked her for phenylketonuria. The baby had developed perfectly, but they had heard the word and were sure their baby had the trouble as the baby was a blond. I said to them, "No, I have not checked the baby for P.K.U. but I can do so. I have found no reason to do that test but I tell you that is a good thing to worry about. It won't occur more often than once in every two hundred thousand people, and I have seen only three cases in the fifty years I have been in medicine." This is a good example of what we all look for; not the obvious, but the abstract.

Are You the Person You Want Your Child to Be?

To every mother I would say: examine your conduct and how it affects your child. Examine your schedule in the home and how it affects your child. Study the diet you give your children. Are you the person you want your child to be? Would you have liked your mother to be the mother you are? Are you busy trying to make a better world for other children and neglecting yours? Are you working yourself to death making money to buy things for a child who is not taught to appreciate things? Are you teaching your child manners, something that will give him or her a better chance than money? Are you really teaching him by example and word the value of a good body? Are you teaching your child to question and to make decisions? Do you speak to your child like you would like to be spoken to? Are you making a nobody out of your child by telling him he is no good? Do you really trust your child and let him know you do? Are you willing to train your child and not leave the job to someone else? Have you taught your child that he must accept the body and mind he has and develop it to its greatest capacity? Have you taught your child to respect other people's rights?

Have you taught your child to turn the other cheek? This was brought home to me recently when a mother brought her little afflicted son in. She had taught him to fight back when he was laughed at, and he was having a difficult time in school. Even the teacher made him stay in the hall because he made a noise she did not like, a noise he could not help. His mind was not too abnormal. I said to him, "You are different from your classmates. You were hurt at birth and you will always be different. We can never change that, but you must learn to live with what you have and make the best of it. Now the next time your teacher puts you out in the hall, say to her, 'Miss Smith, I say a little prayer every day thanking God that you were not born like I was and that you will try to understand why I am like I am.' And when the children mistreat you, tell them the same thing and don't fly into them with your fists and try to fight your way through. When you fight, they tease you to get you to fight more. You can't change your body but you can change your ways and be a happy little boy." It really worked. Teaching a person to turn the other cheek is a hard job but it works.

Are you teaching your child to work, that somebody had to work for everything we have, and that no man has a right to ride on some other man's back? Are you teaching your child that it is a sin not to work and that there are no free lunches? Are you teaching your child how to make money and also how to spend money? A short time ago a mother and father brought in five little boys to be checked. One of them said, "Doctor, hurry and finish with us for we are going to Sears." I asked what they were going to buy. He said, "I don't know but I will find something to buy." I said, "Son, you should learn this one lesson. You should never buy if you have to find something to spend your money for. You should not buy until you need something." A present custom is to give a child allowance money he has not rightfully earned by work and the minute he gets it he has to spend it without any reason or need. This is bad training and may lead later to poverty. Money that comes easy goes easy. A child must be taught to need a thing before he spends his money for it.

If we are to save our country, we must as parents look for the obvious in our children and teach them a constructive way of life. The job is too big to be shifted to someone else. Parents are the God-planned trainers and man has never been able to change this. We have wonderful foster homes and schools that are ready and willing to do all they can to save children but those who operate them will tell you they cannot fill the place of good parents.

Problems in the Teen Years

A parent who really loves a child will look for the obvious when he sees the child showing symptoms that would destroy his chance to have a happy life. Parents bring teenagers to me that are out of hand. They cannot control them. They are heartbroken, for all they have and love has turned against them. The teenager makes big demands the parents cannot fill and will not take orders any longer. These two complaints seem to be the most common. The parents want to know what they have done wrong to cause this sudden and sickening change in their child. And I must say there is nothing that causes parents as much heartache as to see their own child destroying his body or chances in life.

A solemn fact about life is that we can't relive a day of the past. Parents may sit down and go over the past and try to find a reason— and many times may find a reason which now is obvious—but it is too late. They should have been looking for the obvious fifteen years ago, when they were saying, "We must not inhibit this child; we can't say no; he must be allowed to express himself; we must give him what he wants."

Now all of this is clearly obvious, so plain it makes us sick to look back and see where we have failed and how we have destroyed a child and the word "love" was used so improperly. If we had really loved our child, we would have given him or her a chance. I often tell the parents of my patients that if they love a child, they will punish him. Love appears heartless at times. When a child is rolled off to the operating room crying, it looks heartless but we love him enough to hear this crying if the operation is necessary to save his life.

After we dig up all the past with the heartbroken parents and they have found an excuse for their child's behavior, we have not solved the problem as we cannot change the past. We have to take what we have and do the best we can with it. We have children who have been taught a way of life that worked as long as the parents could give all they asked for. Now their demands are to quit school, to have a car and many other things the parents can't afford, and to stay out all night. In the past the demands they made could be fulfilled, but now they are grown and the demands are for things that they should work for. In many instances the parents are not able to give them the things they want.

One mother and father came in to talk about their son. He was born well, the parents were highly educated, and they did not dissipate—parents who would appear to be perfect. But they had been taught that a child should not be inhibited but should be permitted to do as he pleased. The child was cute and his every demand was granted. When he reached the age these demands could not be car-

ried out by his parents, he became a misfit with his school, his
friends, other boys and girls, and then he was called a juvenile delinquent. His parents had been perfect crutches for eighteen years, and
he had never been taught to walk or stand on his own feet. Now he
was a man in size and demands, and the parents were not physically
or financially able to carry him any longer. He was in an apparently
helpless state. What can one advise parents in a situation such as
this? First, they want to know why he behaves as he does. Second,
they want to know what can be done to save him.

One mother said to me, "Doctor, should I run him off from
home? He won't do what we say and his demands are more than we
can fill." To this question I replied, "If he had cancer or some deadly
disease, you would not run him off; and I think he is in a state much
worse than physical sickness. If you sent him away, you could not
sleep at night thinking about where he might be and whether he had
good food or a place to sleep. When you have a child, he is yours
and as long as you live, he will be yours and you will never give him
up. It would be foolish to think that out of sight would be out of
mind, for that can never be possible with a parent."

With the mother and father, we went over the past. I had had that
boy from birth and had tried to advise them, but they did not think
my old-fashioned ideas of inhibiting were good. They would not
love this boy enough to hear him cry for the things that were not
good for him. They were his crutches, and he could do anything he
wanted to do, and they would fight his battles. He was always right;
he was permitted to be defiant; he had to have what he wanted
whether it was a toy, food between meals, his own bed time. He was
not forced to take medicine if it did not taste good.

On and on we could go with the things he was allowed to do and
the demands he made and there was no objection, but now his demands and ways of life are not what the parents think are right. The
lessons that boy should have learned in the past eighteen years have
to be learned at a time in his life when he rebels against orders. There
is no way to go back and start over, but we must take this boy as he
is and try to help him find his way. At this age he has to do it himself.
Parents can't do it for him. They have missed their chance. He must
be told the mistakes his parents made in his training, but he must be
told also that in the sight of God he cannot use his past as an excuse
to break the rules; that no matter how poor his training has been,
he has a mind of his own and he must be the one and only one who

can decide what he will do with his life. He will receive the same punishment as others and will have to pay the same price for the neglect of his body and mind and his misbehavior.

The Teens: the Time to Decide What Is Important in Life

A teenager should be shown that at this age the devil makes his greatest play for his soul of any time in his life and that he must be ready to decide what he wants in life, how he will use the only life and body he will ever have, either for good or for bad. The devil says, "Come on, don't be old-fashioned . . . you are not a child any more . . . don't listen to all that preaching. Follow me and have a good time." God says, "Follow me, and build, not destroy." God creates; the devil destroys.

A teenage child is too big to spank. He has the desires of a man and the wisdom of a child. He must be shown at this age how important it is to make his own decisions and that, if he makes a decision, he must accept the end result.

We should look for the obvious in our children and should not miss a chance to teach them a good way of life before they are too old for us to have complete physical and financial control.

It is very sad to have parents come in to discuss their teenage child, when the parents see that they are not the rulers any longer, and their child is taking a way of life that is not in accord with what they want and think is right.

A short time ago a mother and father came to see me, heartbroken because their only daughter had eloped. The day before, the daughter and young man had tried to talk to the parents and had explained to them that they wanted to get married, but the parents gave them a flat turn-down and said they could not get married until the girl had finished school (she was sixteen). The next day they were married. The parents said many bad things about the boy and the girl—things they cannot forget, and things the son-in-law will never forget—yet they all have to live together. The parents did not look for the obvious. They did not see a girl old enough to move out from under their supreme control. At that age parents must change their approach, but not their standards of right and wrong. If children see a parent break down his or her standards, they lose respect for the parent.

The parents must see in their teenage children persons who are

learning to fly and want to leave the nest and make a nest for themselves. They have adult bodies and adult desires and they are physically large enough to carry out these desires, but they may not be
mentally mature enough to see all the hardships involved in married
life and making their own way. I am sure that is a blessing for, if they
could have all of these hardships shown on a screen, they would still
not believe, and that is good. Whether they believe or not, the hardships of doing without, caring for sick babies, nights without sleep,
no job perhaps, financial troubles, et cetera, must be faced.

Such hardships don't all come at one time, and they are like the
storms against an oak tree. Each storm makes the tree send down
stronger roots. One might say the tree was foolish to start out knowing that it would be hit by storms thousands of times. But the little
tree like the teenager takes the days as they come and grows with the
hardships. And we parents must see this in our teenagers and advise
rather than command. We must give them a true picture of what we
felt and did at their age; how our lives have been, the pitfalls we
encountered, and how we solved our problems. They must be talked
to like adults and must learn how adults talk and act.

When we see a teenager becoming an adult, we must show him
how adults live and use this statement over and over again, "I can
advise you, but you have to make the decisions and be willing to live
with what they bring." Parents should be big enough to let their
adult children solve their own problems and live their own lives.
Many parents will not see the obvious and will walk in where angels
fear to tread and break up a would-be happy marriage. We should
let our married children ask for advice and let them have the chance
to reign supreme in their own home. That is what we wanted when
we started our homes.

When we see our teenagers beginning to want to go out on their
own, we parents must not be so afraid and frighten them of life.
They will get many bumps and broken hearts but they must learn to
walk alone. We must show them that we have faith in their ability,
and that they must look to something greater than parents to hold
them up. They must bring their problems to a God that gives life
and strength to all who will use and develop the life they have in
keeping with their talents and capacities.

Parents Must Be Models

We hear so much today about parents getting down on a level with
their children. Our children don't want us parents to get down on

their level. They want us to be adults and somebody they can look up to. A child has other children his age to play the game of life with and wants his parents to be examples of perfect adults. If a little girl wants to play lady, she uses her mother as an example, so that mother should be the example she wants her daughter to be. Today, as in all the past, many women are not what they want their daughters to be. So the daughter never gets to play lady, for her mother is not a lady. In too many instances she dresses, talks, fights, argues, and behaves like a child. I am sure many mothers have made their sons sin by the way they dress, and their daughters have thoughts they should not have.

Life is one day and it is over. If we have spent that day destroying a child, there is no punishment bad enough for us. If we have spent that day saving a child, we are akin to God and there is no reward great enough for us. To save a child is to save a world. To put children on the wrong road is to destroy a world.

A mother came into my office one day heartbroken. Her statement was, "Doctor, my little son has a killing complex and it frightens me. Yesterday he tied a rope around his little dog's neck and pushed him off the porch, killing his dog. When I came near, he told me he had killed the mean old dog."

Mothers must listen to what they say each day. They can teach a child hate without knowing it. I hear this statement all too often in my office after I have had to do something to a child to hurt him: "Come to your mama—that mean old doctor hurt you." That mother did not mean one word of what she said, for if she had thought the doctor was mean, she would not let a person like that hurt her child. She used that statement to appease a frightened and hurt child and in that statement the doctor became a mean old person to that child and a person to be hated and feared. If mothers would listen to what they say to their child, they might find out where he learned to kill.

When we hear our child cry out "kill him, kill him" at a movie or when looking at television, we have a good opportunity to teach him not to kill and hate. Parents may say before their child, "Somebody ought to kill that person," or "I just hate that man; somebody ought to kill him." They should look for the obvious and then they would not have to ask the question, "Why does my child want to kill or hate?" A child can be taught to love and create as easily as he can be taught to kill and hate.

I see this hate taught and cultivated in broken homes. The mother has been hurt and she teaches the children to hate papa; papa has been hurt and he teaches the children to hate mama. When a child is robbed of that God-given example of the perfect leader, the mother and father, he is handicapped above all handicaps. Then when that child is taught to hate one or both of these guides, he has a poor chance to make a go of it in life. These small seeds of hate that are planted early grow bigger each day and soon become the master of the man or woman. If parents could only see these little killers and haters in my office and know how their lives are destroyed by this deadly disease, the hardest thing on earth to cure, they would watch every word they speak and every deed they do.

Mothers make statements over and over in my office that they do not mean at all, just so-called cute remarks or statements to make the child feel big or important. The statements go like this: "Doctor, he is a little devil"; "Doctor, he has us under his thumb"; "We can't handle him"; "He runs our house"; "He won't mind"; "He just hates school"; "He hates his teacher"; "He hates church"; "He hates to eat"; "He hates to go to bed"; "He hates . . . he hates." Now if we say these things before children a few times, they believe it and they live up to the expectation of the people for whom they are acting. They never trust anybody, not even God. The other side of the picture is so beautiful when parents teach their children to love and create, save and not destroy.

One big problem in this child-destruction process caused by parents who will not look for the obvious is that of parents with a past that they don't want for their children. Recently I had a call from a mother who was crying. She said, "Doctor, I want to talk to you about my child; I have called you about this before and I must see you at once alone." I said, "No, you must bring your teenage daughter who is causing you the trouble. I never talk to a parent about a child without having the child there so I can hear his side. Every child has a right to defend himself." Early the next morning the mother was in my office with her one-month-old baby and her teenage daughter. After a few words of greeting and the ever-true way of getting a smile out of a mother by telling her how beautiful and perfect her baby was, and then a comment on her beautiful teenage daughter, I asked the girl just what happened the night before. She started crying and I told her not to cry but to come on and tell me the whole story so we might try to see how it could have been solved. She said, "We were eating dinner and my younger sister bothered my plate. I hit her. Mother got mad and papa sent me to the basement. Mother came down and started to whip me and I resisted. Then papa came down and used the strap. I am sorry I did that to mother, but this happens so much I could not help it."

Then I asked the mother to tell me what happened. She said, "Martha has told you, but we just can't let this girl come up talking sassy and hitting her sister. My husband and I were brought up by parents we did not respect, and I am determined that my child will not say that about us. We go to church, we have worked hard to give her a clean, beautiful place to live and good clothes to wear—things our parents never did for us—and we are going to train this girl at any cost."

This beautiful teenage girl sat there and wept. Then I said to her, "When a man and woman get married, they establish a kingdom. Mama is queen, papa is king, and their children are their subjects. The parents should reign over this kingdom as long as they live and their subjects should follow the rules of that kingdom until they are old enough to get married and establish their own kingdom. When this is done, the parents have no right to dictate or interfere with the child's kingdom. Now if you were mama, you would expect your child to do as you said as long as she lived in your house. That is the only way a kingdom can stand and be happy and prosperous." The young girl said, "Sure, I would want to run my own house and want my children to follow the rules. I am so sorry about resisting mother last night, but I have a temper and my sister seems to try me out. Mama and papa always take her part because she is younger, but I can't help but fight back when she mistreats me." Then I said to the mother, "You say you and your husband had a past you don't want repeated in your children and all the time you are looking for little clues in this child that might show her tendency to be like you or your husband, and you are so afraid that you make big issues out of normal child behavior.

"All brothers and sisters fight and if a child finds out that the parents will take his part, he picks a fight when the parents are present. We all act if we have an audience. Now the next time little sister starts a fight, let them fight it out or punish both of them. The way people learn to live is fighting with their brothers and sisters while they are children and have the power to forgive and forget. They need to fight and the small child has no right to take advantage of her older sister any more than a sick or afflicted child in the home.

All members of the family, big or little, sick or afflicted, must live by the rules. The statements 'poor little sister,' 'poor little brother,' 'you must not hurt him or inhibit him,' have destroyed his or her chance of being a normal person. So, Mother, let's start over and never speak to this young girl in any manner you would not like to be spoken to. Treat her like you would have wanted your mother to treat you. Prove to her that she is loved and above all, that you trust her and that she is somebody . . . somebody you want to walk with—not drive . . . somebody you want to live with—not as a whipping master, but as a mother. And above all, quit looking for the bad in this girl that you did as a girl. You can't change your past, but you can make a future for this child. If you could just see the obvious: what you are doing is a fight against your past and not a true love for your child's future. Love her and you two live together and be a happy family."

Then I said to the girl, "You have heard all this and now you know why your mother is so strict and afraid. Her past will always be with her and it cannot be changed. Now you are building a past, and some day you will have a daughter. If you make your past ugly, your daughter will have to suffer like you have. Watch every word and every act, for they are recorded in your mind. If you do not build well your past, you will suffer as your mother is suffering, so afraid her child will relive her life. When these problems come up, say a little prayer—'God, help my parents to forget the past and be happy and kind in the present and help me to control my temper and know that everything they are doing is to try to save me from the heart-aches they have had.'"

I am sure this one thing, a parent with a past, has destroyed many wonderful children. We hear these statements over and over again, "My parents were too rich. They did not teach me how to cook or sew, how to spend money, and my child has got to learn these things." "My parents both worked, and I had no home life. I am going to see to it that my child has a mother who knows what is going on." "My mother drank, smoked, was divorced, and I did not have a good example, but my child is going to have a perfect home." "My parents cared nothing about education, but I am going to see to it that my child gets an education." "My parents were over-religious and I am not going to force my child into church." "My parents were very wicked and never took us to church and one thing my children will have to do is go to church."

When a parent's past becomes a big issue, there is often rebellion on the part of the child. When parents are obsessed with a hate for their past, they create in the child a feeling of being watched or not trusted. The one thing above all others that will destroy a wholesome parent-child relationship is a feeling of distrust on the part of the child for the parent or the parent for the child. If a child knows his parents trust him and believe in him, it is hard for him to do wrong, but if he knows they are watching him and expecting him to do wrong, it is easy.

We can't make our child good, but we can help make him bad by making a nobody out of him. Parents must forget their past and live the present as they would like their children to live. They should set up a standard and never break it, learn to say no when it is no and yes when it is yes, never causing their child to doubt them, never recalling their past as a reason for their demands but letting the reason be because it is the right way. They should teach their child that the past is no excuse for the present, that man is made with a mind and he is judged by his acts and not by the acts of his parents or friends. If a man kills, he is not permitted to use his parents or his past as an excuse. God and the State will punish him for murder regardless of his past.

When we see our children drifting, we should stop, look, and listen for the obvious and be willing to face the truth and save our homes. We can't be too careful about what we preach and, if we preach, we must be sure we never preach anything we do not practice. When I started the practice of medicine, I set up one standard. I would never do anything to a child that I would not do to my daughter Mary. I never would send a bill I would not like to receive. It is hard to practice what we preach, for we are so apt to have two standards: one the way we want to live, and another the way we want our children to live.

I knew a wonderful preacher who almost worked himself to death trying to make a better world. He preached against alcohol and other evils that destroy the human body, but he used tobacco. The young people in that church might well have said, "How can he say it is wrong to drink if he smokes because tobacco is just as deadly as alcohol?" We know that many children have sinus infections, earache, and no desire for food because they have to live in a house where they cannot smell food for smoke; and, if they can't smell food, they can't enjoy food. In addition tobacco irritates the nose, making it swell and causing sinus trouble.

Thousands of little children have been forced to go without food and wear sorry clothes because the money that could have provided these things was spent for tobacco. Potential education dollars have been burned up in tobacco, beautiful teeth have been made unsightly, parents' breath made so bad their children could not be cuddled, beautiful mother's skin made brown and "cobblestoned," and cancer of the lungs and lips has robbed many children of their parents. There is not one thing that can be said in favor of tobacco as being a help in making the body better and stronger. Young people may smoke, but they know it is just as bad to destroy the body with tobacco as it is to destroy the body with alcohol, and the preacher, like the parent, must be an example. I am sure this great preacher would have been a greater leader if he had just looked for the obvious and could have seen that the devil used his tobacco habit as a good reason why people should not take his preaching about other vices seriously as long as he had a vice as bad as the ones he condemned.

I heard a preacher say one day he never preached temperance sermons because he smoked cigars. We as mothers, fathers, teachers, and preachers must look for the obvious if we are to be leaders. We cannot fool a child or a dog. My conviction about the Christian religion is summed up in this one statement: we must believe in God and never do anything that will destroy one of his children or ourselves. Anything that harms the body of man is sin and with God there are no little sins; they are all big and have to be paid for. Young people know that, and adults can't make them believe there is a double standard in the sight of God. If it is wrong for son, it is wrong for papa. That is the biggest problem I have confronted in dealing with teenagers. The parents try to teach the child that there are two standards: papa and mama can do it, but the child is wicked if he does the same thing.

Sometime ago a mother came in with her thirteen-year-old daughter. The girl weighed sixty pounds, was thin, pale, anemic, hair dry and unruly, and she had a very sad face. I asked the mother what her problem was. The mother was large and rather fat with pants on that were a size too small and her teeth were yellow. She said, 'Doctor, I can't make this girl eat. She goes to school every morning without a bite, and she will not eat supper. She never feels well and it is hard to get her to do anything." I asked the mother what time she and her husband ate breakfast and she said, "We don't eat. We have a cup of coffee and a cigarette and that is all we want." Then I said to her, "Do you try to get this young lady to eat?" She said, "If I did not force her, she would not eat at all. I have to be after her all the time."

The little girl looked terrible. I examined her and found her body in bad shape, but no evidence of any disease except malnutrition. Then I said to the girl, "This is the only body you will ever have and you must stay in this body as long as you live. You are destroying your body just because your mother nags you about food. You must not kill yourself showing your mother she cannot make you eat. You want food just like any other child, but your mother's nagging keeps you from eating. Now listen to what I say. Life has much in store for you if you take care of this body and treat it right; but if you continue to starve it just to show your mother she cannot force you to eat, you may come up with something that cannot be cured. Don't let your mother's nagging cause you to lose your one chance."

Then I said to the mother, "How can you expect your child to eat breakfast if you and your husband won't eat breakfast? If she needs breakfast, you need breakfast. You should never ask this child to do anything you are not willing to do. Would you like for your husband to nag you about your food? This girl is old enough to know if she wants food and, if she does not want it, you cannot make her eat it. Look at yourself and see if you are the mother you would have wanted your mother to be, and listen to your voice and see if you say the things you would like to have said to you. You two get together and have a happy life. You be the mother you would have liked your mother to be and, Mary, you be the girl you would want your little girl to be. On this basis you can have a happy home. Will you two go home and try this way of life for three months and come back?" The mother said she would and the child seemed happy. If only that mother had examined herself and looked for the obvious, her child's body would not have been starving in a country where there is plenty. This mother did not really love her child and used the feeding as a method to torture her. Many children that come into the world are not wanted and when we find a mother of this type, if we take the time, we can find out the reason why the child is not wanted. We doctors must find out the reason and try to show the parent it is better to forget the past and give the child a chance.

Just recently a mother called me, weeping. She said, "Doctor, John has quit school. He was doing well, but he just decided he did not want to go any more and he has only a few months until he would graduate." (This boy was a patient of mine and had been a very good boy.) The mother stated that she had been angry with him but that had not helped . . . he would not go back to school. He had demanded a car and his father had bought the car or had made a payment on the car, and now all he wanted to do was to drive the car and stay out all night. The father is a poor man and has to work hard to make enough to support the family and provide a place to live. They have five children.

This mother wanted help. Here is a mother with a grown son who had decided he will not go to school, but he will spend his days and nights having a good time while his parents and brothers and sisters work and do without so he can have a car and play. That looks bad and we could not believe a boy would be that cruel to parents who had cared for him for seventeen years. I said to the mother, "You know that neither you nor your husband can make that young man go back to school, for he is physically stronger and bigger than either of you. Your temper or nagging will not help. The law cannot force him back in school at seventeen. Your husband should show your son he is a man and that he loves his son enough to behave like a man. Any man should know that it is not right to take from one child and give to another child who will destroy. So I would turn the car back to the seller and have a conference, the three of you. I would say to my son, 'We are poor people financially, and we can't afford a car for your father to drive to work. This family is a unit and no one child should be given more than another. Tomorrow the car goes back. As long as we have food you are welcome to eat at our table, and as long as we have beds, you will have a place to sleep. We will give you as good clothes as the other children but beyond that, anything you have you will have to get from your own work. We love you and would be happy if you would be a congenial part of the family unit but, if you can't, we have to move on. We can't make the other members of the unit unhappy just because you have decided to take the way of evil and destroy the only life you will ever have.' "

This father did not look for the obvious. He was afraid of his son and tried to buy his love and respect with a car he could not afford. The son lost respect for his father for taking food and clothes from his brothers and sisters to buy him a car he did not need. When this boy found out that his father loved him enough to see him want, things worked out and he went back to school.

Some parents are afraid of their teenager and the teenager knows it. So he makes all kinds of threats to get the things he wants. If parents could only know how easy life would be for them, they would set a standard for their lives and live up to it and never let this standard down. The home is such a wonderful kingdom if it is blessed with a beautiful mother for a queen and a kind, firm, loving father for a king; and the subjects know that the king and queen stand for rules and regulations that parents and children must live by—with no double standards.

Man vs. Pathogenic Organisms

There are many areas in which we should be constantly looking for the obvious. Since the beginning of time there has been a constant battle between pathogenic organisms and man. Man has called this killer many different names: evil spirits, bad air, filth, sin. Man has known from the beginning that under certain conditions his chance to live is better. For instance, if the hands were kept clean and the vessels men ate from were clean, they were a blessed people. The washing of hands and vessels became a religious ceremony or a sacred rite. Circumcision became a sacred rite since the circumcised did not develop venereal diseases as readily as the uncircumcised.

The handling of food was carried out under established laws and any deviation therefrom was a sin. There has been a constant change in customs and as people have found a way to decrease sickness, the new way has been accepted and the old discarded. Man found that the custom of taking off his shoes at the door and washing his feet before entering his house made for better health. The burning of bedding after a person had died, the Indians burning the hut where a baby was born, the burying of all kinds of soiled substances in a home where there were sick people were customs widely practiced.

This continuous fight between man and the thing that kills went on for centuries before man really knew what he was fighting. One day Pasteur discovered the germ or microorganism that was constant in a specific disease, and then the great secret began to unfold and man began to know the real enemy by name for each disease. Then the problem arose as to how to kill this enemy without killing its host. Washing became more important then ever and antiseptics were made by the hundreds. They were rubbed on, sprayed on, and sprayed in the air; they were given by mouth; they were injected into the blood stream, into the spinal fluid, into the abdominal cavity, into the pleural cavity. The life span of man was made longer by these methods, but still sickness was ever present.

The next great discovery was that if man were given small doses of the organisms, dead or alive, in the skin or subcutaneously, the body could build up something in itself to destroy the organisms before they could cause a sickness. This new germ killer was called antibodies and with that man found the way to keep himself free of sickness. Man must have something in his own body, built in him, if he is to stay well, and with this discovery we learned about immunization, the greatest development we have had in medicine, the greatest life saver that has been found up to this time. Typhoid, tetanus, diphtheria, whooping cough, smallpox, polio, measles, pus-forming diseases, yellow fever, and many more diseases are rarely seen any more, for man has built in his own body with the aid of small doses of the killer an army that can protect him against the organisms that once caused sickness or death.

It was found that diarrhoea, typhoid, scarlet fever, undulant fever, streptococcal throat, and many other diseases could be traced to contaminated milk, so pasteurization was required by law. Water was found to be the source of certain diseases so purification of city water was required. Now no city would dare furnish water that was not constantly cultured for organisms. There is constant food inspection throughout the United States, and pure food laws are becoming more and more strict each year. Mechanical dishwashers that sterilize are required in public eating places and where children are kept in numbers. Drinking fountains are a must in schools, and public towels are not permitted. Children are taught to cover their mouths while coughing and not to talk or blow their breath in another child's face. Some schools use ultraviolet rays in the rooms to cut down on infections.

Millions of dollars are spent each year immunizing children and millions are spent to give them clean milk and pure water, but children continue to be sick and it seems at times the most obvious is not seen. In 1924 I remember how upset I would get in doing bacteriology studies when I had a beautiful streptococcus culture growing on a plate of blood agar and a big area of the organisms was destroyed by a growth of mold. If I could have seen then that mold developed an antibiotic, thousands of people could have been saved who had pneumonia, meningitis, scarlet fever, and many other killing diseases. The answer is I was not looking for the obvious. I had penicillin on the plate but could not see it. Today our offices and hospitals are filled with sick people. We have ways to get them well quicker and to immunize, but they continue to come back with bad throats, bad ears, sinus infections, cold, influenza, meningitis, diarrhoea, and many other complaints! With all we have to work with today, why can't we do a better job of keeping children free of disease?

We know that certain people carry these disease organisms in their mouths and throats but are not sick with the disease. They are carriers of the organisms and these organisms are pathogenetic to other people if they have not been immunized against them. These carriers are ever present and if a person comes in contact with the fluid from their noses or mouths and he is not immune to that organism, he will develop the disease. For instance, if a child develops meningitis, we may find that some member of the family is a carrier. We know that the germ or virus of practically every disease can be grown from the throat of that person who is ill with the disease. In the case of polio, when this virus was found in the nose and throat and intestinal tract, very strong antiseptics were used in the nose and throat area when there was an epidemic hoping to prevent spread of the disease.

Now knowing that these organisms may live in the mouth and throat of the well the same as in the sick, I am sure city dwellers have overlooked one of our chief sources of sickness. It would appear that in this area neither the people, the city leaders, nor the public health officials have been able to see the obvious. I refer to expectorating on the street.

Spitting on the Street

Tomorrow when we go downtown in Atlanta, we should take a look at the different kinds of sputum we step in on that trip. We may see blood-streaked sputum from an active case of tuberculosis, thick greenish yellow sputum from an old pneumonia case, yellow sputum from a staphylococcus sinus, the thick stringy yellow sputum from bronchiectisis which may carry a number of different organisms. Then we may see the clear sputum, with no pus but containing organisms and viruses of all kinds from a carrier, and this may be the

most dangerous of all. We are told by some that the big brown tobacco spot is not dangerous, but I would not believe that.

On a warm wet day a woman with thin soled shoes that are kept
warm by her feet can keep this sputum warm on her shoe soles until
she gets home to her rugs. A mother would not let one of her relatives come and visit in her home if she knew he or she had an active
case of tuberculosis, yet she brings in the sputum from downtown
onto her rugs, knowing her children play on the rugs. A mother will
come into my office with a child who has scarlet fever or streptococcal throat, and will say, "My child has not been out or seen another
child for days. How could he get this? We have all been well." She
has been to town and she did not see that big blob of yellow pus she
stepped in as she hurried home to fix supper and give the child the
little toy truck she bought at the variety store on her way home.
Down on the floor the child goes to play with the truck right where
mother walked with the contaminated shoes.

A short time ago I had a very interesting case of meningitis. The
child had visited his grandparents on Saturday along with a cousin
who lived seventy miles away in the mountains. A few days later the
child was brought to my office with a severe case of meningococcal
meningitis. On the same day the mother of the cousin in the mountains called and said her little girl had meningococcal meningitis.
The two children were together that Saturday afternoon and night
and had not seen each other after that time. A thorough study was
made by culturing the throats of all the contacts on that Saturday
and no carriers could be found among them. The children did not
go to town, but the parents did on Saturday afternoon. It would
seem that they must have had the exposure at the same time to come
down with the disease at the same time and the most logical source
was from the shoe soles on that warm rainy Saturday afternoon.

The City of Atlanta, Georgia, has done as much or more to keep
its people well as any city anywhere. Purification of water, good
immunization laws, pure food laws, strict laws about disposal of
refuse, housing laws, laws about the way a home for children or
adults must be kept are enforced. Laws are being passed each year
to give children a better chance to live free of disease, but when we
go downtown and see how our streets are spotted with every imag-
inable kind of sputum, it seems that we have neglected one of the
most important public health problems and one of the most obvious. The buildings have been made so tall in some parts of the city

that the sidewalks have very little sun. If the sun could shine on the sidewalks, I am sure that would help, but with the tall buildings and the many cloudy damp days that we have, we cannot get much help from the sun. Perhaps our sidewalks should be washed, but in a large city that would be a big job.

One might say we should educate people not to spit on the street or sidewalk, but after working in Atlanta for more than fifty years trying to help give little children a chance, I have found that we have a large number of people we cannot educate, and we have to protect our children against those who are not mentally able to learn a clean way of life. This group of people will always be with us as they will go on producing more of their kind. However, we should do all we can to teach those who are teachable the harm they can do by spitting on the sidewalk and street. We can pass laws about this, but such laws would probably not be effective or enforceable. Thus education would appear to be the best approach.

We have a law that man should not steal, but we can't trust the law to keep theft out of our businesses and homes so we have to use locks. We can't trust our pure food laws to take care of all the breakers of those laws, so we wash food and heat food to make sure it is safe. On and on we go with every help we can get to make life safe, yet each individual has to do all he can to make his own home safe. Expectorating on the street is one of our most neglected public health problems and it is up to each person to do all he can to avoid bringing this source of sickness into his home.

♂ ♀

8. Grandparents

Almost daily I hear this statement from a young mother or father, "We know this child does not eat right, but we cannot do anything about the grandparents. We try to train him one way and our parents will let him do as he pleases." It is difficult to conceive of a grandparent ever doing anything to injure a little grandchild's life. But during my many years of trying to help to give little children a better chance, I have seen homes and children destroyed by grandparents.

In a child's life, for the first twelve years, grandparents are the supreme court; they are the perfect pattern. In a child's mind grandma and grandpa have the last word and they can go to them when all other help has failed. When our oldest grandson was two years old, we were visiting in our daughter's home and, soon after we arrived, he came in and got up in his grandpa's lap and started to cry. His grandpa said, "Steven, what is the trouble?" He said, "Pa Pa, Daddy spanked me." I don't know how long it had been since he got the spanking, but I am sure it was not that day. Anyhow, that little fellow at two years of age had learned somehow to believe that his grandpa could do something about the way he was treated by his parents. Mr. Denmark asked Steven what he had done to cause his father to spank him. He said, "I did not come when he called me," Mr. Denmark said, "Steven, if you would do what Grady tells you to do, you would not get spanked. Your daddy wants you to be a good boy and spanking has to come if you are not. Grady loves you and that is the reason he spanked you. He wants to teach you to be a fine boy." Then his grandpa asked him this question, "Steven, if you had a little boy and you called him and he did not come, what would you do?" Steven said, "I would spank him."

We as grandparents have a great influence over these little tots and should make our lives as perfect as possible and be a living example of what we would like our grandchildren to be. As a rule, a person who is old enough to be a grandparent has found a definite way of life and has smoothed out the rough places and given up the things that a parent would not want his child or grandchild to do. As grandparents we are capable and sufficiently experienced to teach our grandchildren how to live. We know the road, we have seen and felt the pitfalls, and we should be the perfect teachers. For some reason that I do not know, these little people love us and believe in us no matter what we do. We as grandparents should take stock of our lives and see if we are the kind of people we would want our grandchildren to be. We get apples off apple trees, and the same is true of people. I have tried to tell a child that what he is doing is wrong but if grandma or grandpa does it, it is almost impossible to make him see that it is wrong. "It were better for him that a millstone were hanged about his neck, and he cast into the sea, than that he should offend one of these little ones." This judgment makes the job of being grandparents one of the most important challenges of our lives. With our influence we can make or destroy many little people.

Why would grandparents ever do anything that would cause their own children to make the statement that because of the grandparents, they could not train their child and develop him as he should be trained and developed? It is hard to believe that this can be true, but it is and it takes its toll. I have studied this problem for years and know it is of great importance if we are to save the child and prevent a broken home. I hear this statement many times, "Doctor, if we ever do anything with this child, we will have to move so the grandparents can't see him." Why should this be true? The grandparents should be a big help and they need the children to keep them young and interested in life.

A grandmother will call me and say, "Doctor, I have the best daughter-in-law in the world, but she is young and doesn't know anything about rearing children. I try to help her but she wants to do it her way." I say to her, "Twenty-five years ago you were young and did not know anything about rearing children. Did you want your mother-in-law to run your life? Your daughter-in-law is as old as you were when your son was born and at that time you were sure you could run your house. Why do you not let your daughter-in-law have the same privilege you wanted? When you got married and started your family, you were the queen in your house, your husband was the king, and your son was your subject. He did as you and your husband commanded until he became an adult. Now that he is married, he is a king and his wife is a queen. Their little boy is their subject, and they have a right to reign supreme in their home. You did not want your mother-in-law to teach your child that you were not capable."

Children must be taught to believe in their parents if they are to feel secure and they can never have this feeling if the grandparents teach them by word and acts that their parents are young and incapable. For a child to be secure, he must know that his mother and father are capable of protecting and teaching him. I have seen this feeling destroyed by grandparents many times.

A mother will say that her child is not to eat between meals and destroy his health. Grandma or grandpa will say that a little bit will not hurt and will feed the child out of schedule. The child knows that somebody has told him an untruth; mama said it was wrong but grandma said it was right; grandma is older than mama, so mama must be wrong; if mama is wrong about this, she is probably wrong about many other things because grandma is older and wiser. With this, something gets started that may never end, for the child doubts his parents' ability and can never feel secure with them. If one could be in my office for a few days, he could see just what I am talking about . . . children that do not trust their parents at all and much of it caused by grandparents who let the grandchild do things that they know the parents are teaching him not to do.

What are grandparents to do when they see their grandchildren being trained by parents who are vulgar, immoral, cruel, selfish? Should these children be taught to hate and distrust their parents? This is a big question and I hear it often. One might say that somebody should come in and take these children and give them a normal chance. As a rule, the grandparents are too old to be just and willing to discipline a child as he should be, and it is just as bad to destroy a child with over-indulgence as to destroy him by deprivation. To take the children away and teach them to hate their parents would create something in them that could never be cured, a mistrust that would go into every walk of life. If we doubt our parents, this distrust seems to go out to everybody and everything.

We grandparents have no right to go into the home of our child and try to impose our way of life, but we must make our lives good examples and teach the grandchildren to love their parents and obey their will because they are their subjects. If grandparents are wise and willing to be examples and not would-be dictators, they can save many homes. The child learns right from wrong and, with his belief in grandparents, he may suffer the curse of poor parents and follow the example of grandparents. One of the heaviest crosses for grandparents to bear is to see a grandchild mistreated by poor parents, but the best way to completely destroy the child's chance in life is to go into that home and try to change it. They are out of bounds; they are aggressors; and they would not have wanted their parents to come in and try to reform their home.

We grandparents should let our children work out their own problems and be willing to see them do without or even go hungry if they are not willing to help themselves.

When people get married, there is a great adjustment to be made by both the man and the woman for they have been reared by different parents. They are two people with two ways of life, two sets of in-laws with two ways of life, and this new home must work out a new way of life. There will be beliefs and habits that are deeply formed by both that will have to be reformed if the two are to live together and be happy. Most couples can do this if they really love each other and if they are permitted to work it out alone. If the in-laws on both sides try to dictate the terms, there is no way to solve the problems that arise, for the in-laws are not in love with each other and are not willing to make any concessions in order to have peace. When a child comes into that home, there will be six people trying to teach him a way of life, so he is all confused and the parents have a hard time. Most important of all, the child may be destroyed.

When our children get married, we should let them come to us for advice remembering that advice given to a person who does not ask for it is often called nagging, and nagging is one of the most diabolic habits on earth. We grandparents should wait for an invitation to enter our child's home. Now that he is married, there are two people to be pleased and his wife should be the one to give this invitation at her pleasure. That is the way we wanted it when we got married. We should treat our daughters-in-law just like we wanted our mothers-in-law to treat us.

The hardest thing on earth for some parents to accept is that their children grow up and are capable of thinking for themselves and running their own homes and making their own decisions. A mother has looked after, fed, and advised a son for twenty-one years or longer, and he has loved his mother and tried to make her happy by following her advice. One day he falls in love and in a short time he is married to a girl who was taught by parents who did not think as his mother thinks. Her son leaves her and is now under the influence of another woman, a person who is to call him her own. The mother has worked for and loved this boy for all of these years and now a woman who has never done anything to build him up has him and, if he really loves her, she will dominate his life and the mother has to give up this choice possession.

One can see how a mother could want to continue to protect her son and insist that he continue to get the treatment she gave him before he was married and, if we will draw on our imagination a little, we can see how a mother could be a bit jealous of her daughter-in-law. Also, if we will draw on our imagination some more, we can see how a daughter-in-law could be jealous of a mother-in-law who previously had complete control of the man she married. Deep down this is the secret of much of the mother-in-law trouble: two women in love with the same man. I think the story about the way Solomon found out who the real mother was in the argument about the baby would apply to the ownership in the case of a married son. Solomon took the baby and said to the two women who were fighting over its ownership, "I will cut this baby in half and both of you will have a part." The real mother said, "Give the baby to the other woman; I had rather give him up than see him killed," and Solomon knew the real mother, the woman who would give her child up to see him live.

We rear our children and never think of the things we have to give to make them as perfect as we can: love, work, money, time. All of these we give freely so that our child will have a chance and then one day we give him up to someone he must love as much as we who made his life loved him. A real mother must love her child enough to do as the mother in Solomon's story. She must say to her daughter-in-law, "He is yours. I love him enough to give him up to run his own life in this new kingdom that must be run by the new king and queen."

It is easy to see how a mother could have an antagonistic attitude toward this person who has robbed her of her most cherished possession, and one can understand how easy it might be for her to do something to get even with this person who is getting the love she once had. Also, we can understand how easy it would be for the mother-in-law to give her grandchild something that would cause annoyance to his mother, something she would not have given to her own child, and let this grandchild do or say things she did not let her own child do or say. As parents, we love our own children enough to hear them cry for things that are not good for them and we are not fighting anybody when we make them mind; but we cannot love our grandchildren as our own. That is impossible. We may pity them and call it love, but love will make us punish our own children and make us see them suffer if it is for their own good. Love appears cruel at times and we grandparents must learn the difference between love and pity.

Grandparents will say to me, "Doctor, my son and his wife are young and they don't know anything about rearing a child, and I am sorry for the child." I tell them that their attitude toward the child is not love but pity; that their parents were probably saying the same thing about their child when he was a baby, but they did not want the parents to interfere.

As grandparents, we must study our acts and search deeply into our subconscious mind to see why we treat our grandchildren as we do. Is it love or is it a method of getting even with our daughter-in-law for taking over the love and domination of our son, or son-in-law who lords it over a daughter who has been a little princess to us? No mother can really give her son or daughter up, but love is long suffering, and a true mother can play the game so well she will never do anything to hurt her daughter-in-law or son-in-law, or her grandchildren.

I hear this statement over and over, "Doctor, my mother-in-law still thinks she must look after my husband and she just can't let him alone or give him up." I say to this mother, "You love this little boy you have above everything on earth and you are willing to do anything to make him a good mind and body and a good way of life. You will work night and day to make him happy. Then one day he will tell you he is getting married. Will you be willing to give him up in the same way you are asking your mother-in-law to give her son up? In just a few years you will be where your mother-in-law is today. Don't try to make your husband give up his mother for he can't. He will always love her as a mother and love you as a wife. You must play the game fairly, listen carefully to all she says, and never ask her advice unless you are willing to follow it through. You can never love her as a mother so don't be a gusher. Never try to impress her with your complete domination of her son."

The sure way to hurt a woman is to hurt her child. Children have been used time and time again to hurt parents in broken homes. Papa will do something to the child he knows mama doesn't like, and mama will give the child liberties that papa dislikes. Grandparents will do things to grandchildren that the daughter-in-law and son-in-law don't like, for in that way they can hurt the person they dislike.

At night when I turn out my light and crawl into a clean snow white bed, soft and smooth, in a room warm or cool just to my liking, free from odors or insects, I call it a little heaven. Then all of a sudden I become sick and heavy of heart when I think of the millions of little children in this world who are going to bed in filthy, tobacco smoke filled, insect infested rooms, in the slums, sick, hungry, pot-bellied, anemic, child and parent filled with hate and fear, with harsh talk from drunk demon-possessed parents, or parents that are so mentally retarded they cannot do any better. I sometimes hear people say, "Oh well, it takes all that to make up a world, and we must accept this for there is no way to change a world; it was planned that way." The people who say that are those like myself who have the good things of life. God never planned anything to destroy a child. Man and the devil are the planners that create the conditions to cause death and destruction, and to say every evil and vulgar act is God's will comes from the devil. We mustn't ever say to our child that these conditions are God's planning, for it will teach him to hate a God of love.

Why was I not born in the slums? I had a grandmother who was left with two little girls to rear and she was willing to work for fifty cents a week, plough and hoe a garden, make the food they had to eat, and sell eggs to buy the clothes she did not weave from the cotton she grew, and she saved the fifty cents she made each week to pay for an acre of land that was to be cleared by hand. She continued to work and buy land until she had four hundred acres and a good home for my mother and aunt. She taught my mother and aunt that it was a sin not to work and a sin not to give thanks for work; that a person must be willing to work for what he can get, and not put a price on his worth, but do every job as though he were working for the Giver of all things. I was saved the tragedies that have befallen so many children because of a grandmother and a mother who believed in God and work.

I have worked with many unfortunate children through the years and most of these would not have been so if the grandparents and parents had lived according to the laws of God. There is work for everybody if we are willing to work for what we can get for our labor. We can keep and feed our bodies on very little of this world's goods and teach our children a good way of life. Some of the finest and happiest children I have ever known were children with parents who lived by the laws of God and worked by the laws of God. A person can't fail if he lives this life.

The clinic in which I work one day a week gives food and medicine regularly to little children who have grandparents and parents who are chain smokers and/or alcoholics. They are dirty, smell bad, and will not work, but by some means they get tobacco and alcohol although there is no money for food, clothes, or a clean place to live. I see grandmothers come in with short shorts, tight pants, hair frazzled, teeth brown from tobacco smoke, breath bad, skin "cobblestoned," persons you would not like to come near you, yet they are little children's grandmothers.

How could a child with such a grandmother have a chance? I can remember that when I was a child some of my friends had grandmothers who dipped snuff and how ashamed these children were of them. Today, some of the grandparents look and act much worse than those snuff dippers did. How can we solve this problem of frightened, sick, neglected, heartbroken, hungry little children who had no choice of parents or grandparents? It was not the plan of God that any child should suffer. We human beings brought this on. God never made a neglected child and He never made hunger or hate. We have made all of this by doing the things we want to do rather than the things that are best for us and our offspring. Why will not human beings reason?

We grandparents have an important place in the lives of all young people in providing an example of how a life should be lived; but to our own grandchildren we owe a special debt of right living, for we are responsible for bringing them into this world and should do all in our power to give them an opportunity to develop lives that will be happy and fruitful.

♂ ♀

9. Teaching a child manners, decorum, and customs

"Train Up a Child in the Way He Should Go . . ."

From birth to the grave, life is built of precept after precept and line after line. There is no way to live yesterday over. The opportunity to teach the things we should have taught our child yesterday is gone. Every day has its own problems, and these must be solved when they present themselves. It is the nature of man to learn a thing when it is necessary for his existence or welfare.

All races and all countries have customs and manners that are proper for them. Every family has customs and manners that are proper and necessary for its members to feel secure and well adjusted. If these customs and manners are to be continued in the nation or family, they must be taught and taught from birth. We can't take a little Catholic boy at ten years of age and tell him that from this day he is to be a good Presbyterian; and we can't take a ten-year-old Presbyterian boy and tell him that from this day he is to be a good Catholic. Ten years have passed in their lives and they can never forget or blot out what they have been taught and have experienced. They may be able to see things in a different light by constant study, but they still remember the things they were taught from birth.

Today many children are not taught by their mothers day after day the manners and customs of their family and race. This job is often turned over to a maid or to a nursery school while the mother is out working for some other person, in an office, school, church, child guidance organizations, child health organizations, doing P.T.A. or club work, or engaging in many other endeavors. She is giving her time and thoughts trying to make a better world for her child to live in, but is missing the only chance she will ever have to mold her child who is to live in the world she is trying to make. It is like a hen that would leave her little chicks out in the cold while she goes off to build a nest and finds after the nest is built, her chicks have died from neglect. No, a hen would care for her chicks and pull the grass in and build the nest while she protected the chicks.

Values have truly shifted in our country. We who practice medicine hear the sad stories of mother after mother who has missed the opportunity of teaching her child a way of life until it is too late. The child can't wait until the mother has time to train him; his training is far more important than other things and cannot be postponed. An untrained child does not fit into the world she is trying to build. This statement I hear day in and day out, "Doctor, I don't want to leave my child and neglect his training but I do want my child to have a better chance than I had." What is she saying? Does she mean she wants her child to have a better chance to have things? Things are important but things cannot bring happiness unless the child has been taught the use and value of things.

I see parents who are slaves to their children when it comes to getting them things, clothes, cars, trips, parties, things in general, and many of these young people are unhappy because they have never been taught how to appreciate and to be thankful for things. Children that have the most things seem to be the most dissatisfied, because the parents have neglected the most important thing on earth, preparing their children to live with people and things. A child has to be taught everything. He has to be taught fear, love, hate, personal rights, security, honesty, truth, race customs, family customs, respect, religion, language, and many, many other things. There is not a particular day for us to say, "This is the day to teach my son not to be afraid." This is a process of continuous teaching.

The minute he was born and he was placed on his back, his arm fell back and he was frightened of falling. If he had been placed on his abdomen as every little baby should be, he would not have had to get this shock so early, before he had had enough experience to know what it was all about. If he had been handled gently like a cat handles her kitten, this fear could have been eliminated while the gentle movements of his mother would have taught him that when his arm dropped, he was not going to fall. Each day the way the baby is held, the type environment he is subjected to teaches him that his mother and father are not afraid and there is no need for him to fear. Having his food on time and at regular intervals, he has no fear of starving. With a time to sleep, a time to play, a time to eat, he feels secure. He does not fear punishment, for he knows what to expect. Insecurity comes only with not knowing. If a child does not know how his parents are going to respond to his acts, he lives in constant fear, but, if he knows that a certain act will always bring out a certain response, he is a happy child even though his parents may use a very painful method of punishment.

When a child is reared by a maid or in a nursery school where there is no right to discipline like a mother or father, he will be like the person who trains him. One of the hardest things to get across to parents of an adopted child, or grandparents who are left with grandchildren to take care of, is the difference between pity and love. If an adopted child commits a breach of discipline, the mother or father may say, "That poor little fellow; I can't stand to punish him." The same is true of grandparents, maids, and nursery school teachers when they are left with children that have been deprived of their mothers by choice or circumstance. These foster parents will often say, "I just love him too much to spank him." If that child were their own, spanking would not be hard to do at all if he were doing things that were not in line with the best manners and customs of their household.

We punish a child because we love him and want him to have the right training. Pity comes in at times when a child is born to a mother and father who did not want him in the first place, and they tried not to have him. Then the "poor little fellow" attitude comes up in that person who knows the child was unwanted, and he pities him instead of loving him. No matter what the situation is, whether the child is adopted, a grandchild, an unwanted child, in a nursery school or orphanage, or a child deprived of the love and care of his own mother, he should never be the object of pity. He should be loved enough to make him do without things that are bad for him, and must be punished for breaking the laws and rules of the home, school, or state. As we punish him when he transgresses, we should praise him for his good deeds, and never use the term, "Poor little fellow; I love him too much to train him right."

In dealing with children, we must be sure we have learned the difference between love and pity. A child hates pity but will always respond to love. Children that are pitied have a difficult time learning how to love. Love, if true, sometimes appears heartless, even cruel, when it comes to training a child. To see a child cry for something that would harm him would not break down a mother who really loved that child. To see a child go through severe pain to save his life is bad, but a true mother or father would be glad to see this if it saved the child. We must teach our children this type of love, love that cannot be changed by tears. Learning how to love starts from the first day of life, and each day the child lives, this lesson of love grows deeper and deeper if the parent is a sincere teacher. One cannot fool a child.

You Can't Buy a Child

In the case of many neglected children, the parents try to show they love them by showering them with gifts, never coming home without bringing something. A child that is permitted to want because his papa can't afford to buy has the utmost respect for that parent, because he knows that his father loves him enough to see him do without if it is best for the child and the family. Teaching a child to love is a painful process at times. We must see our child want things that are not good and not have them, and we must see him punished for misdeeds and not apologize for the punishment. Love never gives over to persuasion if it is not good for the child. The insecure child is that child who knows he can get what he wants by a cry or a temper tantrum at times. When his parents are not the only persons he has to depend on for his happiness, his cry and temper tantrums will not work any longer. These children grow up to be insecure, immature, and it is too late to change them. They have been taught one way and society demands that they live another way, and they cannot adjust. Unteaching is much harder than teaching. A neglected plant can never be what it would have been if it had been started right and that is true of a child. Life is built up one day at a time. A child who is taught good manners and customs from birth has a treasure that money cannot buy.

When a child at six starts to school and has learned from his parents how to say yes ma'am, yes sir, thank you, good morning, how are you, yes please, no thank you, have this chair, you go first, let me help you, I will close the door; to get up and offer a chair to an older person; to listen when talked to; to never interrupt a conversation without saying "pardon"; to let a lady enter the door first; to stand firm on an issue when he knows it is right; to respect rules and regulations of the school; to feel that school is a privilege and not a task; to know and respect other people's rights and other people's property, and recognizes that other people have a right to their own opinion; to stand firm in the way he was taught right from wrong: he is truly the child of choice and should be because he will be the leader of tomorrow. He may not be the leader of the majority of the people, but he will be the leader of the group that wants a better world in which to live. When children of this type become men and women, they can speak with authority and people will listen.

Children of this type are not in the majority today; far from it. In the past fifty years I have seen this class gradually decreasing and the insecure and immature type steadily increasing. We can't get enough schools built to take care of the children we call maladjusted, immature, insecure, and we can't get enough prisons and detention homes for them after they become adults. All of this goes back to some human error. We must remember that we cannot get a perfect baby from two dissipated parents, and we cannot get a well-mannered, well-adjusted child from poor-mannered, maladjusted parents. It has to be taught, and taught by example as well as by word every day, and taught by people who practice what they teach.

If the first six years of a child's life are spent learning from his mother, father, grandmother, grandfather, the way of life they want him to take, that is hard to change. In the first six years of a child's life, parents make or break him, for it is during this time the most important things are learned: manners, fear, hate, love, faith, all the things that count in making a person secure or insecure, happy or unhappy, well or sick, and maybe I should say rich or poor.

One custom that has meant so much to children should be revived: the custom of story telling and reading to them. A little boy on his grandfather's lap listening to a story about when grandpa was a little boy is a beautiful picture. In that way children have been taught important lessons, and there is no better way to help a child to develop his imagination. A story read by a parent or grandparent to a little child with the lesson that comes in the story is a good way to teach. A child that is started right will sit for a long time on a parent's or grandparent's lap listening to a good story. There can never be any better training than this, and children who live in homes where mama and papa, grandma and grandpa have time to let them relax on a good soft lap and teach them by the story method, are truly blessed. No parent or grandparent should ever be too busy to miss this greatest of all opportunities. A child who has a good story or a sweet little song at bedtime will not likely have nightmares.

As a student, I always had great respect for a teacher who made me feel that he knew more than I did and could speak with authority, and when in the classroom of that type teacher, my respect for him would have kept me from doing anything that was not proper. That is so true of parents. Children who respect and love their parents were taught this by their parents being respectable and honorable and never admitting that the child was a problem too big for them to handle. If a mother storms out at a child, we can watch that child when something goes wrong. He will use the same response he has seen his mother use and then he may be punished for an act he learned from his mother. A child can't help being confused if he has parents who teach him to do what they say to do and not what they do. Papa eats with his hand, brother must use his fork; papa blasphemes, but little brother gets a spanking if he uses the same language; papa smokes, but little brother gets the strap if he is found smoking; mother gives a party and all those present drink, smoke, and talk about the neighbors; but if the children do any of these things, they are punished and may be referred to as juvenile delinquents.

If we could only practice what we preach and never demand more of our children than we demand of ourselves, we could be a happy people.

We have some beautiful customs and manners in this Southland of ours that are fast getting away. These manners and customs have made our homes, our churches, our communities, our towns, our cities, our state and country, happy places in which to live and have fellowship with one another. These customs and manners must be taught in the home by the parents and grandparents. We must teach our children the way to eat, the way to walk, the way to sleep, the way to talk, the way to dress, the way to meet people, the way to keep house, the way to make money, the way to spend money, the way to treat their elders, the way to treat their superiors, the way to read and what to read, the way to worship God, and many, many more things.

The proper way to eat is getting to be a lost art. Many homes have changed their kitchens into snack bars with tall stools and eating has become a short order restaurant type operation with each person giving the orders and mama or papa filling the orders. How different it is when the meals are prepared and placed on the table, with the family all seated at one time, and papa gives thanks to God for what they have to eat! They are taught by this one act that eating is a privilege and not a task. The table is a wonderful place for a family meeting and a great school. Table manners are important for a person to get the most out of life, and mean much in the way the food is digested. Poor eating habits mean poor digestion, and good habits must be taught by example and by words.

There is no better place to teach a child to be reverent than at a well-supervised eating table. I talk to mother after mother about the way she feeds her family and so many times it goes like this: "My husband gets up at 6:30, makes himself a cup of coffee, and goes to work; I get up about 8:30 and fix a bite for the children that go to school and after they are gone, I get up the smaller children and fix them what they want."

I always say to them that when a man goes to work without breakfast prepared by his wife and does not have his children eat with him and tell him good-by before he goes to work, he has a wife who is not worthy of the money he makes. A man who is willing to go out and put in a day of hard work to make a home and provide food for his family surely deserves a good breakfast and a word of thanks before leaving each morning.

Children brought up in homes where mothers do not teach them that papa works for them and should be loved and respected, go out to establish the same type homes. No matter how sorry papa is, he would not object to a word of thanks from the family and a "Papa, have a good day; we love you lots." One of the first things I am interested in when a new patient comes in my office is how the members of the family eat, when they eat, and what they eat. The body cannot protect itself against disease unless it is fed right. Unless our eating habits are proper, our health cannot be good and if our health is not good, we are not happy. Table manners and customs may make the difference between a happy home and a home of confusion and poor health.

Casual Living and Fast Schedules

This is a day of casual living. We have casual clothes, casual houses, and casual everything; and casual means without care. We cannot rear a family that way and make it happy. If we are casual eaters, we help buy doctors and undertakers casual cars. Life is exacting and there is nothing about it that can be casual. Our children should be taught that way if they are to be happy.

Our stomachs digest food in a certain way and have been doing it a certain way since man was created, and we cannot change this at all. The stomach retains food for a certain length of time until it has finished the gastric digestion and additional food should not be added during this process. So, the person who says, "I will be casual with my eating and will eat when I please and what I please," soon ends up with poor health and a doctor's bill. We cannot change nature and anybody who breaks the physical, chemical, or moral laws always has to pay the price. These laws are not casual. We should give our child a chance by teaching him when to eat, what to eat, and to be grateful for what he has to eat.

Working fathers and mothers today operate on a fast schedule. They get up in the morning thirty minutes too late, rush through breakfast, in many cases have only a cup of coffee, get on a super highway and drive several miles to the office. At nine-thirty or thereabouts they have a coffee break and consume two cups of black coffee; back to work until twelve-thirty at which time they have lunch, drinking coffee or tea with the meal; then back on the job until mid-afternoon when there is another coffee break; back to work until four-thirty, and then a fast trip home. If we count up the amount of caffeine and nicotine they have consumed in an eight-hour period, it would be more than six grains of caffeine, and perhaps an equal amount of nicotine. By this time they are so tense they must have a little alcohol to quiet them down, then at dinner they take more coffee or tea and nicotine. If they go out or have guests, they continue to drink and smoke until they go to bed and in some cases a sleeping pill is needed to get a night's rest.

How can we teach our children a good way of life when we live like this? How can we have patience to teach our children manners and customs when our bodies are constantly in a state of tension and each little cry or question seems to be the spark that sets off an explosion of temper with maybe a slap or a brutal scream? I see the little children of such parents in my office and they are a sad lot. They have never had the chance to learn a quiet, peaceful way of life. All they have known is rushing, loud talking, snapping, slapping parents. There is no way to help a child in a home like that.

When I was a child, girls were sent away to finishing school to learn manners and customs that would make them gracious ladies and good homemakers. This was a good custom, but all of that could have been taught at home and was taught by mothers who could not afford the school. Girls and boys alike should be taught how to walk correctly if they are to have efficient bodies. Maybe man once walked on hands and feet, but that is not the custom today. The way a person walks has much to do with the way his clothes fit, the way he feels, the way he digests his food, and the way he is accepted by society. If a person walks with his shoulders slumped and his abdominal muscles relaxed, the viscera drops down and cannot function as it should and clothes don't fit. His appearance may make him miss a good job or keep him from getting a good wife. Children must be taught what it means to make a good physical appearance, and walking or standing plays an important part.

When school days start and the children have to get lessons, numerous problems arise in many homes. When should they get their lessons? When they get home, they should get out and play, or do the work that is required of them, until around five o'clock. By then they will have been out and away from school work long enough to be able to study again. Then they should get their lessons before dinner and be ready for bed soon after dinner. As they grow older, they do not require as much sleep and may have to do some studying after dinner, but that is not as good a time to study as before dinner.

Teenage children need more sleep than they are getting today. Good sleeping habits have to start from birth, and as the child grows older, he should not be tempted by things in the home or outside attractions. Children today old enough to be interested in radio, television, movies, scouting, clubs of many kinds, or sports, have little or no chance to get the required amount of sleep. They see their parents doing without sleep and they feel like they have no right to be told that they need sleep.

We parents may say we don't need sleep any more, but that is not a true statement. Every person who expects his or her body to function at its best must have sleep, at night if possible, and it should be at least eight hours. We may never go back to the idea that night was made for rest as we have the excitement of the night to attract us, but parents should teach their children the value of sleep if they are to get out of their bodies the best that is there.

Somewhere along the way the human being has been taught that it is a rebellious act to stay out all night and, as children reach the teens, it is a great brag to say, "Oh, we stayed out all night," or, "We did not get in until morning." There is no more reason why a person would brag about being out all night than being out all day if it did not make him appear to be rather wicked. Maybe the saying that man loves the dark more than the light because his deeds are evil still holds true. Children who see adults stay out all night use this example to show their parents that they have grown up and can do likewise, that they don't need sleep, and that they can get out of the night what adults get out of it.

We should start as soon as a baby is born teaching him how to talk the language he is to speak. When a baby is brought to a mother the first time, she talks to him as though he could talk back. She will say, "You are beautiful," or, "You are just like your papa," and papa will say to the baby, "You are just like your mama." Both parents talk to the baby every time they are together and by the time the baby is three months old, we can see him fix his mouth, raise his eyebrows and answer back in a voice all his own, trying his best to talk as he sees and hears his parents talk. This talk should be plain, well pronounced, and in the type grammar the child will be expected to use. If baby talk is used, the baby learns the wrong words and incorrect grammar. Then when he begins to talk, his parents expect him to use the proper words and grammar, which is not what they taught him. It is much better to train right than it is to untrain. If a child is taught to speak baby talk, that will be his language until he is old enough to know that such language makes children leave him out in play and laugh at him because he talks baby talk. Children can be spared many heartaches if parents will teach them proper language instead of baby talk.

I do not say that parents should not talk in endearing terms to their children. On the other hand, it is important that they do so for children learn how much we love them by the way we speak to them and what we say to them should be in good English and good grammar. If children were taught to speak clearly, slowly, and distinctly, a great deal of the stuttering and stammering that cost the parent much worry and expense could be avoided. Children should be taught never to speak when others are talking. This all-important lesson in good manners seems to have vanished with adults and seems sure to go with their children.

Learning by Listening

We cannot learn if we have not been taught to listen and this teaching must come early. A child should be given audience, but he must learn early to take his turn and that we learn by listening, to always speak in an even voice, not to ever raise his voice when angry, and to speak kindly to everyone.

The principal source children have from which to learn how to talk is the people who care for them and that is why every child should have the person who is the ideal for his life to train him. This cannot be left to someone who cannot speak correctly and expect the child to be better than his teacher. The ability to speak well and properly means as much to a human being's happiness as any other one thing. A child in school, a man in his office, a mother and father in their home must know how to speak to get the greatest response from those with whom they speak. If a parent knows how to speak to the child, the discipline problem is largely solved. If a man in business knows how to speak to the employees, they can't do enough for him. If a man in his home knows how to speak to his wife, and vice versa, there is rarely any dissension.

In the schoolroom the method of speaking is the difference between an effective teacher and one who destroys a pupil's chance to learn. Every day we see people in all walks of life who think the world is against them, that they are mistreated in school, hospitals, stores, church, wherever they go, all because they were never taught as children the art and manner of speaking to people. This important part of life must be taught from birth and the parents, by word and example, are the proper teachers.

The art of meeting people must be taught. Often in my office I speak to a child only to have him sit there in a sullen manner and not respond. Through training, this attitude in the child must be changed if he is to be well adjusted later in life.

Sometime ago I was invited to a home and had an opportunity to see what this family had accomplished in a short time. They showed us a beautiful office with everything that could be bought to make it perfect for a businessman. As to the home itself, there was a television set in every room, the beds were self-styled, the floors were covered with the best carpets. Then we went out to see the cars— two of the biggest and finest. Then we had a visit with the family.

The little three-year-old boy sat there alone on the floor playing and did not speak to us or show any interest in our speaking to him. He did not say one word to us the entire evening. When dinner was announced, he did not come to the table but got a dish of corn flakes and walked around over the house eating them, his only food for that meal. He was pale and pot-bellied.

This family had everything it takes in a physical way to be happy, but they neglected the thing that would have brought them the greatest happiness. In addition they have handicapped a helpless child in not training him in a way that he could be happy. A child at three should know how to meet people and should be taught by that time good eating habits. This child is three years behind and, when he enters school, he will either be a bully or will shrink back and not be seen, for he has not been taught how to meet people and how to make people love and admire him.

The first day in school for a child who has not been taught how to meet and respect his elders may be his downfall. The little boy who enters school and is able to say, "Good morning, Miss Smith, how are you?" and when Miss Smith says, "How are you, John?" and he answers, "Fine, thank you," and he says, "Yes, thank you," "No, thank you," "Pardon me," "May I have," "Yes, sir," or "Yes, ma'am," and many more phrases of culture and refinement that have to be taught the first six years of a child's life, is off to a good start. A child must be taught a gracious manner and an attitude of respect for his age and his elders if he is to be accepted by his elders and his age. This training has made life easy for those who practice the art and lack of it has made life difficult for all too many boys and girls.

It is easy to love beauty and love, but it takes a good actor to accept the vulgar and untrained. Many times in all walks of life we see a person who may not be the most capable one in the group, but that person knows the art of meeting people and is happy and makes others happy. This must be taught from birth through training and it cannot be taught from books.

We have a casual way of meeting people now that is not good. We go to a party or to any place where we meet people we have not met before, and the method of introducing the stranger is, "Mary, meet Jane." When we meet people, we want to know who they are. Maybe Jane has worked for years to get a husband so she can be Mrs. John Smith, the wife of the office manager. She has earned a title and she should be introduced as Mrs. John Smith, the wife of the office manager. Then we have something to start on; we know she is married and her husband is an important man. Meeting people is so much more pleasant if we know who they are, i.e., Mrs., Miss, General, Colonel, Major, Doctor, Lawyer, Cousin, Aunt, Uncle, Teacher, Husband, Wife, and it is no trouble to introduce a person in a manner that makes the guest feel good and saves many embarrassing situations. They have a title and they are somebody. "Jane" or "Joe" really means nothing.

Casual introductions have caused no end of embarrassment. After people work for a title, they should be honored with that title and, if they are our kin, we should let our friends know. This "Mary" and "Jane" method of introduction and addressing each other takes much out of people. That method of addressing people should be the privilege of the most intimate friend. To meet a person and have him or her call you "John" or "Mary" is just a little too presumptuous. That privilege should be earned rather than grasped at the first meeting. The saying that familiarity breeds contempt is true, and our children should be taught by our example to address people by the right title and should be taught to address their elders as Mr., Mrs., Aunt, Uncle, or by the title they hold.

The child must be taught the value and importance of a well-kept home, the way to keep house, the way to make a home. We cannot walk through a flour mill without getting a little flour on us, and a child cannot live in a well-kept house without learning that this kind of house means less work and more efficiency.

When my child was small, she played with a little girl down the street. After one visit she said, "Mama, Mary's house looks like they closed the doors and shook it up." The way a house is kept makes a lasting impression on a child's life. Today when the "wise" leaders in the so-called psychiatric world teach casual living, they are preparing a race of people for a great deal of unhappiness. A baby that is not taught from birth a system and that man cannot live alone in this world which was made to operate on exacting precision has a hard time. When a child who is taught demand feeding, demand sleeping, demand dressing, demand keeping of his room, visits in his playmate's home where there is a mother who believes her home came with a price and must be orderly and well kept, he soon finds that he is a misfit and is not wanted.

Then comes school. He has done everything on a demand basis, and now he meets a teacher who is trying to help forty children and she must have a system and rules. He must keep his desk neat, he has to stay in a chair, he has to wait his turn to speak. Now this poor little self-demand child is really in a tough spot. After many years in the practice of medicine and having the mothers of these children coming to me for help, I can say that self-demand living has been the downfall for what could have been many fine people.

We should never teach our child a self-demand way of life and expect him to be accepted in a world that is governed by precision methods. A self-demand person would have to be alone—a hermit— to be happy because people will not tolerate a person who cannot conform to the golden rule that we should do unto others as we would have them do unto us. A child who is taught that it is right to satisfy his own desires and never take into account how much he is hurting someone else, has a poor chance in life.

The Child as a Measure of What His Home is Like

I have seen family after family like this in my years of trying to help in giving children a better chance. The home looked like a jumble and the children looked like the home. I have had one of these mothers come in for help, and I would give her a good outline on how she could make her den of confusion into a home if she would only try. First, put the house in order; make it neat and clean with the help of her children. Second, serve her meals at normal intervals regularly spaced and see that everybody eats at the same time, with a word of thanks given for the food. Third, keep in effect a regular bedtime, a getting up time, and a play time.

I have seen some of these homes change in a short time and, greatest of all, I have seen the children show marked improvement. A child is the best barometer to tell what a home is like. The minute we see a child, we can picture the home he lives in. I was talking to a friend a few days ago who was comparing some of our American women with the Queen of England, and he said, "You must remember that Queen Elizabeth was trained to be a queen." Oh, that we American mothers could see the value of that statement and train our children to be kings and queens in their own home, and give them a fair chance in the competitions of life.

A child who is reared in a jumble cannot think as clearly as a child who is reared in a home where there is order, cleanliness, and good system. The habit of putting the toys up, cleaning his feet before coming into the house, washing hands before handling food, hanging up clothes, keeping shoes polished, and keeping things in the right place, will determine to a large extent the kind of life the child will live as an adult. We cannot stress enough the value of a well-kept house in the rearing of a child; the keeping of the house means the keeping of a life.

Teaching little children a system, a custom, a manner of life is the best investment a parent ever made, and it pays the greatest dividends. Without a system, no home or life can function well. Keeping house is a wonderful school in which to teach the child that there is a time and place for everything and that for things to be of value, they must be in the right place at the right time. A toy in the wrong place may mean a visit to the hospital or doctor, or possibly death. Medicine in the wrong place costs the lives of many children.

A child should be taught that the house he lives in is his home, and he should not be paid to keep his room or take out the trash or wash the dishes. He should be taught that he should contribute to this place he calls home and he should be happy to help. If a child is paid for all he does in a home, he is in the same position as a hired servant, not a member of the family. He learns in this manner to receive and not to give. The child learns the art of making a contribution to life by helping his parents keep a neat place in which to live. It is poor training to pay a son to cut the grass or work on the farm. He is not a hired man, but he is working for himself, and he should learn this lesson at an early age.

If a child works outside of the home and earns money, this should be his, and he should be taught how to spend his money. Children should be taught early that they must not spend all the money they make if they are to be good business people as adults. They should be taught that a portion should go back to the Giver through their church to help people who cannot help themselves and a portion should be saved for a time when they may need it to pay for something that takes a big sum. Then they should learn how to invest and make money and the great lesson of buying things that are worth what they cost. A child should learn to say to himself, "Do I need what I want today more than I will want what I may need tomorrow?" Children must be taught that there is a tomorrow that will have needs like today, and that money saved today will make happy tomorrows. They should also be taught that it is more blessed to give than to receive. This is a hard lesson to learn but, if started early, it can be learned. They should be taught that a selfish person is never happy, but the greatest happiness comes when one makes others happy.

In this day of television, radio, movies, and many other things that serve an important place in life, the reading habit is almost lost in many homes. There is no better way to develop the mind than to read and visualize and construct the things we read. If we see a play on the stage, we see it all and we don't have to use our powers of imagination. The construction power in our brain must be exercised if we are to create. Reading is the greatest of all methods of developing this important part of our life.

Babies seem to be soothed by reading or singing and as soon as they are able to talk, they like to be read to and have us tell them stories of our childhood, as they let their little minds fill in with their imagination. Soon they can tell us imaginary stories that show that their minds are developing. A child that is read to and talked to and has stories told to him soon wants to read and get into this wonderful world of thinking things out and solving problems in his own mind. Progress is built on imagination and this imagination cannot develop if we see it all like we do on television and in the movies. We have to read and then fill in, think out, visualize, determine in our own minds how it worked, learn to want to solve problems and figure out things on our own. Reading to be enjoyed must be started early with the right book presented at the right time.

Selecting the right book at the right time is the parents' job. Great problems can be solved by people who were taught from childhood to think. Books should not be brought in the home that would teach children hate, distrust, unfair play, a lack of reverence, vulgarity, dishonesty, or any lesson we would not like our child to learn. As we read, so we live.

Children entrusted to our care should be taught the decorum, the manners, the customs that would give them the best chance to be good citizens and the best chance to be good parents. Then each child should be taught that after all the help his parents have given him and all they have done to make his life a success, he himself must select his way of life and must decide what road he will take in life. The road to better the human race or the road to degrade the human race are his choices; to be a builder or a destroyer. Parents can't make these choices for their children for the reason that each individual has been endowed with knowledge and wisdom to enable him to make his own decisions. The most vulgar, immoral parents in my office would select for their children a perfect life if they could give it, even though they were not willing to be examples and give them a chance. But the child must select his own way of life.

♂ ♀

10. Natural laws:
The laws of the Creator

There are three groups of laws we cannot disobey without having to pay: the physical, chemical, and moral laws. Disobedience to these laws has meant unnecessary suffering and death to thousands of children. No matter how much we would like to change or do away with these natural forces, they will remain true as long as the world stands. These laws are not enforced by the federal or state government or the church. They are laws that must be taught from birth.

There is no federal, state, or church law that says a mother will be tried for murder if she leaves her newborn baby on a bed that has no sides to restrain him and, as a result, the baby meets an accidental death. Yet I have seen a baby that crawled off and wedged his head between the wall and bed and hanged himself. There is no law to punish a mother who leaves her child in a high chair while she turns her back for a moment and the child falls out, fractures his skull and never develops mentally. There is no law that says a mother should have a high latch on the basement door to save her child from falling down the steps and breaking a leg, arm, or skull.

The amount of suffering caused by neglect of the physical laws could not be estimated. The same is true of the chemical laws. There is no state law that says if a mother leaves the aspirin bottle where a child can get it, she is guilty of murder if her child eats the aspirin and dies. But large numbers of children die each year from this drug that ordinarily is so harmless. The same is true of Clorox, the cleaning fluids, and hundreds of other items. The mother will say, "I just turned my back and he had it." Then it is too late. The chemical law was made along with man and will last as long as man.

A little boy has destroyed his friend's best toy, has carried home his only pet, and has said his friend set the fire that destroyed property when he really did not. These moral laws he is breaking are laws that have not changed since the beginning of time. Newton saw an apple fall and gave us an example of physical law. Socrates drank the hemlock and gave a good example of the chemical law. David took Uriah's wife, breaking a moral law, and it went down in history as an example of what such an act costs.

Every person, when confronted with a problem too great for a human to solve, calls on some higher power. Some call this higher power the sun; some the moon; some Mohammed; some Buddha; some the Great White God; some the God of the Hills; and some the God of Heaven. A person may tell you he has no god, but I am sure that if he should see his child dying, he would make an effort to call on some power greater than himself.

When a child is born, we start teaching him these natural laws of life. These laws come so easily for a parent to teach it is routine to keep saying all day: "If you touch the hot stove, it will burn; if you go near the edge, you will fall; if you drink that, it will make you sick; if you take your friend's toys, you will be punished." With a good mother, a child could never tell you when he learned these laws. The mother teaches the child that medicine must be put out of reach, that cleaning fluids are not to be swallowed, that poison for insects must be put out of reach. There is continuous advice from the adults to the children that these things are hid or put up high so as to save them much possible suffering. Day after day these lessons are taught, and the child can never tell you the day he learned not to eat roach poison or go too near the edge of the precipice.

The moral law is taught the same way and the teaching must be started at birth. The little baby must learn that with certain behavior he gets a certain response. As he gets older, he will find when he brings in a toy that belongs to his playmate, his mother is not pleased and he is taught that taking things from someone else is morally wrong; also that he would not want that to happen to him. When he tells his mother a falsehood, she explains to him that it is wrong. Then as he grows older he begins to think things out for himself. He begins to ask questions: Why is it wrong to tell a falsehood? Why should I not steal? Why should I not drink cleaning fluid? Why should I not take what I please? When a child begins to ask questions, he must be given answers. When he was tiny, his mother and father provided him with the human reasons why he should obey the natural laws. They were his god and goddess and in his little mind they could do all things. His father was strong enough to protect him against harm and his mother was kind enough to protect him against want.

Now that he is older, he must be given a stronger reason why he cannot break the physical, chemical, and moral laws. It is at this time that we teach him religion. We show him that parental strength is not adequate to solve all of our problems and enable us to understand these great laws, so we seek strength from a higher source. The child must be taught what this source of strength is and this teaching should come early. The earlier a child is taught that his parents have a source of strength to help them carry on in the face of tragedy and disappointment, the easier it is for him to be secure.

A child should be taught by word and example the religion the parents believe in and that religion should be a definite religion if the child is to feel secure. If the parents are not sure of what they believe in as their source of strength, then the child is sure to be confused and insecure. If we started out with a guide on a mountain trail we had never hiked before, and the guide announced, "I am not sure about the bridges on this trail or the falling rocks on the cliffs and whether they are safe," that hike would not be at all pleasant. No one would want to take a chance with a guide like that. But if the guide met us with a smile and said, "This is to be a great trip; I know the trails; I have been over them and they are safe," it would be easy to follow him. No hiker would want to miss that trip. If we are insecure, we cannot teach our children to be secure. The frightened, screaming, seemingly devil-possessed child is the product of insecure parents.

Parents: the First Guides

Parents are the first guides a child has to put him on the right trail and make him feel secure, and they must be sure they know the way. A child must not see his parents shake, cry, and tremble when they have to face a problem. He should see and hear them say, "There is one way and only one way and that is the right way," never seeing them do wrong because that seems to be the easier way out; never hearing them say, "I know this is wrong but this is all I can do this time." To be in my office for a day and see how these little frightened, insecure children suffer because they have never been taught that they can trust, believe, or be sure of anything, is a distressing experience. They were not born that way, but were born to parents of that type, and they had to be taught. In order to be secure, the parent must have a definite belief and must live it every day.

We hear a great deal about the Roman Catholic Church and how hard it works to make Catholics out of the children of its members. The church has a definite plan and the only plan that will work. The child is taught from birth that he is a Catholic and that his religion is the right religion. The children are started in the church early and they are taught prayer, the love of Mary, and the love or fear of God. When we check them in the hospital immediately after birth, we see a symbol of their religion pinned on their gowns. The child sees this symbol on his body as soon as he is able to notice, and sees it on the wall in his room. He sees his mother and father go to mass regardless of what comes up and as soon as he is old enough, he is taken to church and sent to a church school. All children can be taught the moral and religious laws of life if their parents believe and practice these laws.

We who are Protestants should not criticize the devout feeling of Catholic children toward their church for it is as much a part of their life as their parents. You cannot convince them that their religion is wrong any more than you could convince them that their mothers are no good. The things we learn early are hard to unlearn. If we Protestants want our children to be Protestants, we can get a good lesson from our Catholic friends. We can't teach our children a religion or the laws of God by working at it one hour on Sunday morning with perhaps another hour on Sunday evening. Children must be taught from birth on a full time basis if we are to build up in them a true belief in anything. If they are properly taught, it is not easy for them to follow after false leaders and every ism that comes along.

We hear people say that every child should have a right to live as he pleases. It sounds very democratic to want every child to be free, but freedom is a curse if the free person is not taught that to be free and have freedom he must know how to use the privilege in a way that he will not make a slave out of another person. A child cannot be free until he learns that freedom is not safe unless he learns how to respect the freedom of others. The prodigal son was given his freedom but he did not know how to be free and soon found that the freedom he chose was worse than being a slave.

We have a free country. We are taxed to educate our children in a common school, and we believe the state should pay for the education. In that case the state can and does provide the teacher who teaches our children. We cannot say the child must be taught by a man or woman who obeys the moral laws. A teacher cannot in truth teach anything he or she does not believe. The teacher has the children six hours per day for five days each week or more time than the parents have with them while they are awake. The teacher has more time to influence the child than his parents have and, if the child is not trained in a true belief for six years before he goes to school, it follows that the teacher may change his entire outlook on life. We hear from many persons that some particular teacher was the reason for their success in life. The teacher has the most important job on earth next to the parent.

A person preparing to practice medicine is under the influence of teachers for some twenty years. Thus one can appreciate what it means to be a teacher and why parents should be sure of what they themselves have taught the child for the first six years. After the first six years, the parents should know what the teacher is and what he is teaching their children. We can't say to our children that they are to be Baptists, Methodists, Catholics, or communists. The children can't become such on command but must be taught, first by their parents and then by their teachers.

The Ten Commandments

God gave us life and laws to protect and perserve this life. In the Christian religion these laws are spelled out in the Ten Commandments. If a child is really taught the Ten Commandments, and he believes and lives them, that child is secure. When a child is taught he must have no other God but the living God and he believes that, he is always a secure person. He knows if he is profane, he must be punished, so he speaks and acts with reverence and avoids profanity. He reads the entire Commandment in every case including the one about the sabbath that reads like this: "Keep the sabbath day to sanctify it as the Lord thy God has commanded thee; six days thou shalt (shalt means compulsion) labor and do all thy work." We must teach our children to keep the sabbath, to take that day to rest the body and to get spiritual strength for the coming week.

The second half of this commandment is just as important as the first half if the person is to be secure. We hear sermon after sermon about not working on Sunday, but I can't recall a sermon about the sin of not working six days out of the week. It is just as sinful not to work six days as it is to work on the sabbath.

If this commandment were kept, there would be no want on earth and no occasion to teach our children they cannot expect to get free lunches. They must be taught that everything we have, somebody had to work for and that it is a sin not to work. They must be taught that nobody owes them a living, that they must work for what they get, that they cannot ride through life on a boat built by someone else, but they must make their own. They must be taught that work is truly a gift of God and is something to be thankful for, not something to be feared; something we should want to do, not something we have to do; that work is not a punishment but a pleasure.

Honor thy father and thy mother. How can a person honor something that is not honorable? This commandment should make parents do some soul searching for if they are not honorable, they make their children sin. The commandment is read to children and when it is taught, it is directed to children. This is good, but the commandment to be fulfilled must be practiced by the parents.

We must always think things through and decide what the conditions are to make a thing work. It is not enough to tell a child he should be good; we must give him the example and the reason for being good.

Honor thy father and mother is a commandment with a promise that we may have a long life. Have we seriously thought about this promise and how it works out? How can we honor our parents or God? What can your child do to honor you? Would it be to tell you each day how much he or she loved you? Tell you that you are the greatest person on earth? That you are kind and beautiful? Bring you gifts? Write you each day? Come to see you often? All of these things are good and a parent would not object to any of them, but this is not what a parent wants of his child to determine if the child honors the parent.

If your daughter comes to see you every day, writes you every night, brings you all kinds of gifts, and each time she comes her breath is bad from tobacco, her teeth brown, her skin "cobblestoned"; if she is carrying in her body a little baby that has to smoke one to two packs of cigarettes daily; if the prospective mother is not eating right: Could you say this daughter was honoring her mother? The mother had carried this daughter nine months, did everything she could during that period to make her little baby a perfect body, and after she was born, the mother was never too tired to prepare the proper food, answer all the questions, nurse her back to health when she was sick, and dress her body warmly and beautifully. That body and life she was so proud of has now been spoiled by dissipation and made unattractive and ugly, and each day she is destroying the thing the mother had given her life for, a child that she could be proud of, a child about whom people could say, "That mother did a beautiful job in rearing that girl and she has been a blessing to this world."

The best way we can honor God and our parents is to take the body they have given to us and make of it a blessing to all mankind, using that body as a living example of what we would want our child to be like. If we would take the body and the life our parents have given us and make it as perfect as our parents would have it be, we could not help but have a long life. So the fulfillment of this promise can come only to that person that will never do anything to his or her body that would make it less efficient. My child could never make me believe she honored me if she mistreated the body I helped build. I don't believe God can or will answer a prayer made by a person for good health if that person is doing things to make his or her body weaker.

God said, "Present your body a living sacrifice, holy, and acceptable unto God." A body cannot be holy if it is subjected to things that are harmful and killing it by degrees. It may be too much or too little food, it may be tobacco, alcohol, caffeine, harmful drugs, hate, too much rest, or maybe too much work. If we are to honor our parents, we must show them that we love them enough to take care of what they have given us and to give to others the chance we have had. If we could get preachers to practice what they preach and parents to practice what they teach, it would be easy for a child to honor parents and God.

I know a girl who has never let a day go by without writing to her mother. This girl smokes two packs of cigarettes a day, never lets a day go by that she does not take alcohol, never eats right, and her mother is heartbroken to see the body she worked so hard to make perfect being destroyed by dissipation. That mother would give up all the letters, all the "I love you" if she could see her daughter using the body she made as she had dreamed she would. We can't make our parents believe we love them or God believe we love Him by telling them of our love. We have to prove it by our behavior.

Thou shalt not kill. This commandment, in my opinion, is the most poorly kept of all the moral laws. It commands that a man, woman, boy, or girl should not kill a human being. The commandment means you should not kill yourself or your neighbor. This is the one commandment that doctors could do much about if they would practice the law themselves. Parents try to teach the child it is wrong to kill and the child sees the doctor, mother, father, preacher, doing things that are injurious to their bodies, things that will eventually kill them. Eating too much or irregularly, drinking things that will injure the body, smoking, chewing tobacco, driving too fast, working too little or too much. This commandment did not say, "Thou shalt not kill fast or slow." Too many people interpret it to mean, "Thou shalt not kill fast," when it is just as great a sin to kill slowly. Slow killing is not feared like fast killing and slow killing has a large following. One reads in the paper that John Doe jumped off the river bridge and killed himself. He has sinned and people talk about him and comment on how foolish he was and wonder how a preacher could preach a funeral for a man like that. On the same page of the paper one reads that another John Doe died of cancer of the lungs from smoking or cirrhosis of the liver from alcohol, and nobody seems to think he has done wrong, or has been foolish, or is disgraced or that it would be difficult for a minister to preach his funeral. In the eyes of God he has killed himself as much so as the man who jumped off the bridge. A child should be taught that the human body is the home of the soul and that the body must be kept clean and well by eating good food and thinking good thoughts, that to mistreat or kill one's own body is just as sinful as to mistreat or kill a neighbor's body. We teach our children that a doctor can cure, but we should first teach them that it is wrong for them to do anything that would make the body sick.

Man has known the moral laws since the day Adam ate the apple, but the devil kept him so confused that these laws had to be spelled out in the Ten Commandments and so stated that there could be no doubt as to what the laws were and stated so clearly a child could understand them. Doctors, preachers, parents, pope, or government may give the right to break one of these laws, but God has never changed one of them and never will. If we are to be happy, we must obey them.

Thou shalt not commit adultery. Thou shalt not steal. Thou shalt not bear false witness against thy neighbor. These laws all come under the same plan. We should never do unto others things that we would not want them to do unto us. This is one of the hardest laws to learn.

Boys should be taught that all girls should have the love and respect that they would want for their own mothers, sisters, or daughters, and that every girl, no matter how bad she is, is somebody's child. They should be taught that God will punish a man for breaking a law with the lowest type of womanhood as much as He would with the highest type. If she has no character, the offense is no less. A girl should be taught that a boy or man will always respect and honor a lady. That has been true since the beginning of time unless a woman tempts a man or shows herself willing to sin. Man will always respect her if he is mentally normal or not under the influence of something that causes him to be unable to exercise self control. Good women make good men and a good world. Bad women make bad men and a bad world.

The law of possession has to be taught by example. This law can be taught very early by the parents. A child with an older brother must be taught that his brother has things, that he has things, and that they both have things. He can't have or destroy his brother's things, his brother can't have or destroy his things, and they share their things. The law of possession is important and should be emphasized to children at every opportunity whether it be taking things or destroying things that belong to someone else. When a child sees his father cut a Christmas tree off somebody's land without asking permission, he sees his father steal. His father might say, "Oh this doesn't matter; he doesn't need the tree," but the child has learned in this example to take things that don't belong to him. The child should be taught that stealing is wrong no matter how little the act is.

False witnessing. It is easy to teach a child to tell an untruth. Parents tell them all day. A mother will say, "I am not going to town," and will slip out the back door and go to town. She will say to her child, "If you cross the street, I will whip you," but he crosses the street and she does not whip him; "If you do that, I will tell your daddy," and she does not tell him; "If you don't eat your vegetables, you can't have the cake," yet he does not eat the vegetables but he gets the cake. Day in and day out children learn they can't trust their parents to tell the truth. We must watch what we say and be sure we tell the truth if we are to teach our children to tell the truth. Little false witnessing like a little child grows bigger each day.

Children should be taught that what we have we should work for and that we should not want what the other person has; that we should make our own and not take his. To envy and covet is easy. If a child wants a toy that belongs to his friend, he must he taught that the toy was bought with a price and, if he is to have a toy like that, he must be willing to pay the price.

Life is just one short day and for that day to be happy we must teach our children a religion, a way of life that is right for us and for our neighbors. We must be willing to educate our children in schools that teach them the way of life we think is right. We can't send our children to a teacher who breaks all the moral laws and expect our children to obey such laws. If our state schools employ teachers to teach history, grammar, mathematics, reading, and writing but they cannot teach the moral laws, our children should not he subjected to these teachers unless we are willing to accept the product they turn out. We can't live with a person as long as a child lives with a teacher without getting something from the person, good or bad.

In our society of today we have come to believe that to make a better world we must give people things, good houses, good food, good clothes. One thing we must know is that we cannot make a person better until that person wants to be better, and we cannot help him until he wants help. The training of a child for a good way of life must be started by the parents at birth, it must be cultivated by the teacher, and refined by the church. We can't wait for the school or the church to do it all but we parents must take the lead and teach him that to obey the laws of God brings happiness and to disobey always brings the opposite. It matters not how often our doctor, preacher, teacher, friends, parents may tell us a little bit of transgression will not hurt; we still have to pay for every law we break. Man has passed laws that make it legal to break every law of God but in the end they are still the divine laws and, if broken, the offender has to pay.

We cannot make people good by giving them things. A child that

has plenty never asks for food. It is much easier to help a person that
wants help than a person that is self-sufficient, and that is why so
much is done for the person who is down and out, and the rich
person may never see that he needs God or man until it is too late.
A child has so many wants it is easy to teach him that all things work
together for good to those who love the Lord and keep the holy
laws.

Today we are digging deep into the unknown. There is no end to
the amount of research to find out the unknown: why we are sick
and then how we can combat this sickness; why man can fly and
how he can keep from falling; how we can devise weapons that can
destroy the world, and then how we can invent something that can
counteract that force. Then we want to know about this creature we
call man who is finding out all these great wonders of life. What is
he? Where did he come from? Where is he going? Why does he
behave as he does? One will spend his life making a good thing;
another will spend his life destroying a good thing. Why would two
men behave so differently?

Voltaire once said. "Men who are occupied in the restoration of
health to other men by the joint exertion of skill and humanity are
above all the great of the earth. They even partake of divinity, since
to preserve and renew is almost as noble as to create." Why will man
not want to preserve and renew? The return is so great and is the
only source of real happiness. Yet we see our prisons full, our homes
wrecked. Scientists have been able to work out a true working formula for all known chemical and physical measurements. They can
tell you exactly where a planet will be at a given time and the depth
and height of space. Man has a formula for solving all these problems but he has never been able to figure out man, what he will do,
or how he will react under certain conditions. The problem solver
has never been solved. The psychiatrist and the psychologist have
tried to break into this unknown field, and the theologian has
worked hard at the job. Still one can hear a mother say, "Why are
my children so different? One will build; the other will destroy. We
gave both of them the same food, clothes, home, and love. How
could they be so different?" The psychiatrist can dig into the very
bottom of a child's past and can always come up with an excuse for
his behavior and that is the thing a mother wants to know, just why
her child behaves as he does. After the excuse for his behavior is
found, then the child must be convinced that his behavior has been

caused by someone else or something else and it is not his own fault. Then he can put the blame on that person or thing and he is supposed to quit doing the thing that is making him different and making his mother unhappy.

This is a way to teach a person to pass the buck and it has brought many people into a state that could not be tolerated by the law or by the people this person had to live with. Is this a good way to teach a child? It has been tried since the beginning of time. If a boy fights, his excuse may be like this: "Johnny would not let me ride his bike." If a thief kills, he will say, "The man of the house tried to stop me."

Accepting Responsibility for One's Acts

Children after they are old enough to reason should be taught not to try to put the blame for their acts on somebody else. They must be taught that in every person there are two forces, good and evil, and these two forces make people different. There is a constant conflict between these forces in man. This conflict causes a person to be mentally sick, lose sleep, feel sick, yet no doctor can find anything wrong physically. The thing that takes away sleep and appetite, the thing that makes a person feel insecure, is that constant fight within, knowing right but doing wrong. A person goes to doctor, lawyer, preacher, parent, friend, trying to find somebody who will agree that what he is doing is right when he knows it is wrong. If the doctor or other counselor agrees, he feels better for a short time, but still the force that tells him he must do right if he is to be happy continues to fight within him, and the insecure person begins another quest to find someone to sanction his wrong way of life or someone or something to blame for it. I have heard patient after patient say, "My doctor said my smoking would not affect my baby before he was born and that I could smoke, drink, or do anything I wanted to do." I say to her, "What did you really think about the situation? Did you honestly believe what you were told?" I have never had the first mother to say that she did not know the answer before she asked the doctor. She wanted to put the blame on the doctor and she did. She will always say. "Why did my doctor not tell me the truth?" Every day these questions are asked of the doctor: Can tobacco harm me? Does alcohol injure the baby? What about sleeping pills, dope, tranquilizers, coffee, eating between meals, eating too little or too much, and thousands of other questions?

When the patient gets the doctor's approval, he goes out feeling better but in reality he knew the answers before he asked; and now he has no respect for the doctor who agreed with him, but he does have the most important thing on earth to him, the feeling that the blame is now on the doctor. He said it was all right so he should be held responsible. This does not make the patient suffer any the less. His alcohol, his tobacco, his casual living, his going out on the town and getting it out of his system, his expressing himself and letting his temper go, living it up; all this he may do but he still has to pay for all the wrong he does. The chickens do come home to roost.

The average human being knows right from wrong, and the God in us tells us what is right. The devil in us tells us what is wrong, and we ourselves only can decide which way to go. We can search to the ends of the earth trying to find out why man behaves as he does, and we find that it is all summed up in man's power to be able to know right from wrong and make his decisions accordingly. Man ate of the fruit of the tree of knowledge, and since that day he has known good from evil. Today we are trying to make man believe that he does not possess this power and that all of his acts are the end results of some outside influence or experience. We hear a mother say the reason her son has trouble in school is that the boys call him fatty, skinny, dumb, lint-head, brain, square, sissy, and many other names. This is not the reason but just an excuse she digs up when she is trying to find out why he is failing, why he has started smoking, drinking, driving too fast, destroying what someone else has created. This boy knows right from wrong, and he has decided in favor of wrong and uses excuses to justify what he wants to do.

I have mothers bring their children in from time to time making this statement, "Doctor, something has gone wrong with my child; he will not go to school; he will not study; he will not keep his room"; and many more "he will nots." I say to the child, "Tell me the truth; why don't you go to school?" He will often say, "I don't want to go to school and mama said she could not make me go." They will always tell you the truth. You don't have to go any further and look for some sort of complex. He doesn't want to go to school, and his parents can't force him to go. What more is there to work up in that case? Men or women drink because they like to drink, and they like the sensation they get from nicotine. Why do we have to go searching in all the old dusty attics for skeletons to use as excuses for a man's behavior when that man is doing exactly what he wants to do? God or the government does not go on this search. If a man robs or kills, he is punished for his act; and the law doesn't ask about the relatives or which side of the track he lived on. In the eyes of the law a man, no matter what his past has been, has the right and responsibility to decide for himself and must be punished for his misdeeds even though he may try to put the blame on his family and his environment.

You hear a story that is not true about a person. Something in you says to keep quiet for that is none of your business. Then something in you tells you to defend this person, for by tomorrow the story will be on its way and possibly it can't be stopped. If you keep quiet, you will not be able to digest your food, or to sleep, but if you defend this person and save his or her name, you feel all warm inside.

When a person comes to a doctor with all kinds of conflicts and insecurity, if the doctor will take out his Bible and turn to the Ten Commandments and start with the first one and go to the last and let the person study each one carefully, he can analyze his own case. He can find out what the fight is all about and what law he is breaking to give rise to this fight, and can find himself and be able to put the blame on the right person and that person will be himself.

Practice What You Preach

No parent should ever try to teach something he doesn't believe or practice. Preacher, priest, and teacher should never try to teach children to follow the moral and civil laws if they themselves are not willing to live up to these laws. If we could get parents, preacher, teacher, and priest to do as they say to do, then we could get our children to believe and respect these laws. It is not uncommon to see a preacher preach a sermon on temperance and walk out of the church and start smoking. How can a little boy believe his mama when she tells him he should not smoke. This is just one example, but the point we must remember is that our children are getting more confused each day and that the true followers of the right way of life are decreasing.

A child must be taught that, if he wants to do wrong and he follows advice that sanctions his action, he will still have to suffer for his wrong. The fact that all his friends are doing wrong will not lessen his punishment. He must learn that the way to be happy is to understand early in life about the two forces in the human body and to always decide for the right. These young people should be taught to analyze their own cases. Has our job, our money, our position, or other people become our God? Is that what causes the conflict? Let us think deep and pull out the truth. Are we reverent or have we learned to take the name of God in vain to show men how great we are? This is one of the chief ways to diagnose a person with an inferiority complex; he talks big and vulgarly to show he is a big man.

I read in the paper some months ago a statement by a young woman. She said this: "Sure, I had a baby out of wedlock; what the heck; that is nothing new and it does not matter." Her child will have to change the subject of conversation all his life about his parents, and his children about their grandparents, and on and on it goes. Boys and girls must be taught that all other boys and girls, no matter what their color, race, or kind, are their brothers and sisters in the sight of God, and that to molest or mistreat one of them is to hurt one of God's children, for which a price must be paid. The good in boys or girls will tell them if they break the law, they will have to pay. The evil will say, "Go ahead; what the heck," as the young woman said.

Did you steal somebody's good name by gossip or by not defending him or her? Did you pass your school work on the knowledge of somebody else? Did you keep your friend from working and steal his time? Did you take something you did not work for? Did you tell a falsehood to save your face? To tell the truth and the whole truth is hard at times and that is one conflict that has caused much deep suffering. It is easy to twist the truth and, after the act is done, it is hard to correct. Is the force that is causing the great conflict in your life envy? This is a great fight in relation to our brothers, sisters, mother, father, schoolmates, and friends. We see them with things we would like to have but we are not willing to pay the price to get them, so that temptation can cause a great internal fight.

To sum up this chapter on the natural laws it may be said that all comes back to the word faith. Fidelity to one's promise or allegiance to duty or to a person; loyalty; that which is believed; belief in God. If our country is to stand, if our children are to grow up secure, if our churches are to grow, if our God is to be revered and followed, we must have faith; we must believe in those things we want to be lasting. We must teach our children faith from the day they are born. Faith is not something we can buy or find in a book or just let come.

Faith comes with knowing, and knowing comes from seeing these things work out.

The Security That Comes From Faith

If we lose faith in our parents, then lack of faith begins, like the proverbial snowball, to grow bigger fast. It is sad to see a mother come in with a spastic or an abnormal child; but to see a child that has lost faith in his parents is far worse. You can hear them crying before they come near the office, "Mama, will Dr. Denmark stick me?" The answer is often, "No"; and then comes another loud cry, "Mama, will Dr. Denmark stick me?"; then another, "No, Dr. Denmark will not stick you." On and on this will go until they leave the office. The child continues to cry and ask the same question over and over. The mother has never told the child the truth and he can't believe her now. The mother will say. "I can't understand why he is so bad and why he is so afraid of doctors; all children are not that way." He had to be taught to be afraid of doctors. This little child was started wrong. He had never learned to have faith in what his mother says. She did not carry through with what she said and made promise after promise that was false. He was frightened because he did not know what to believe, and he continued to ask the question over and over again until he had nightmares.

There is no way to ever make this child as secure as he should be for he has lost faith in the greatest teachers on earth, his parents. This same child when he starts to school is afraid of the teacher and will not trust his playmates. When taken to church, he cannot be sure the things his mother tells him about the church are true. When he enters college, he still carries with him this lack of faith in people, and eventually he loses faith in business, government, and country. Such a child has something more dangerous than any disease, a thing that will cause him more unhappiness than anything else, the tragedy of not having faith in anything. This lack of faith goes on to his home, his wife, his children, robbing him each day of that wonderful feeling that he can trust his family, his friends, his government, his country, his God. Hundreds of these children are going out into life with chips on their shoulders, confused and doubting. The one common theme of their lives runs about like this: "This is just my luck"; "No more than I expected"; "The other fellow gets all the breaks." A life spent with such an attitude is worse than being physically handicapped. Somebody taught him to doubt. Somebody taught him not to have faith in man or God.

Then we have the baby that is born to a mother who has a purposeful way of life. She knows what she wants for her child, she has a goal. It might not be what another person would think is the best way of life but she knows where she is going and she makes her baby feel that he is in safe arms and nothing can harm him. His father is strong enough to protect him, for the father knows what he wants out of life and where he is going. There is no condition or circumstance so bad that this child does not have faith enough in his parents to believe they can carry him through. This to me is the most beautiful thing on earth. These children who come in my office are happy. They know they are going to get a shot, but they never cry until they are hurt and then not for long. Their parents will say, "That's all right; it won't hurt long." I always tell a child the shot will hurt and I always tell him to watch me give it. In that way there is no deception. He knows what to expect.

When this child goes to school, his parents tell him school is a good thing and he believes it. It will not be a bad old school or a mean old teacher. Then when it comes to the church, he believes what they tell him and he learns by example that the church is good and can make his life better. Later when he starts a home he will trust his wife and children. No person can be happy if he does not have faith in his country, his fellow man, and God.

All of this is a process of evolution from the cradle to the grave. Faith grows like doubt. Once a life of doubt is started, it is almost impossible to stop as each step the child makes increases this doubt until he has no faith in himself, anybody, or anything. These are the people that the counselor, psychiatrist, and clergy are trying to rebuild if they are to get anything out of life or make any contribution to this world. Parents should realize that these little children they teach to doubt may be the downfall of all the people that come after them, that a doubting child may become a doubting mother who will rear another doubting child, and the process may go on to infinity. The same is true of faith. I see mothers and fathers every day who were reared by good parents and are now rearing good children.

To teach a child to doubt is hell; to teach a child faith is heaven.

With all I have said about training, we must not forget that man has been endowed with the power of making decisons, with knowledge and with wisdom. We cannot understand a child's behavior, no matter how well he has been trained, if we disregard this power he has to make his own decisions. There are two forces in him, and these two forces are there pleading their side when any suggestion is made. Whatever the suggestion is, these two forces are on the alert and not a second late, no matter how small the suggestion might be and no matter how good the training has been.

If the training has been good, the decision is easier to make because the child knows a way. Whereas a child who has been reared in a home with no specific pattern of life or perhaps a casual way of life, and has not been taught a fine line of distinction between right and wrong, finds it harder to make a decision when a problem arises.

We have to come back to the real truth about our conduct and know that man commits sins because he wants the things that are sinful more than he wants the things that are right. If a child does not want to go to school, we say he has a school phobia. We will not admit that the child has a mind and the power to make a decision. We begin to dig in to find some psychological reason why he doesn't want to go to school. The parents are examined, also all their past life is reviewed, until we find something to blame for the child's dislike of school. I say that a child can dislike school no matter how he was reared or what the past life has been. He has to make a decision and he decides he does not want to go to school. If you talk with the child and really get down to facts, he will admit that the dislike for school is his own decision.

Adam blamed Eve in the Garden of Eden, but that did not lessen his punishment. Adam's past had been perfect. It is just as true today as it was then that man is endowed with a mind and some force inside that always tells him the difference between right and wrong and he is the only person that can decide which side he will take. We can talk, we can put in prison, we can give things, we can give money, we can whip, we can promise, we can deprive, but we cannot make a person stop what he is doing until he decides for himself that he will stop. We hear a person say, "I wanted a medical education but my parents could not send me to college." Just as in many other decisions, this person put the blame on his parents for his failure to get a medical education. No, if he had wanted a medical education,

he could have worked it out. It was much easier to decide that his
parents should take the blame and that he should take an easier way
of life.

Man can make excuses and try to put the blame where he likes,
but the conflict in his own body will continue to torture him until
he gets on the right path and takes all of the responsibility for the
discipline of his own body. Then he can be a happy person. It is easy
to tell someone else how to live, but to make our body and life toe
the line is a hard job. We see an obese child come into the office and
the mother all upset over his excess weight. She has nagged for
months about the amount the child is eating. The child is normal
and rebels against nagging, and the very sight of the mother suggests
food. He just has to eat to keep those in his audience on the edge of
their seats. If they should cut down on the food, the show would lag
and no good actor would like to see his audience falling asleep. So
the act goes on. This child must be checked to see if his fat is due to
some physical defect. A good history on the family helps and tests
are made to determine the metabolism. After the examination and
when history has been obtained and there does not appear to be any
physical reason for the obese condition, this is my approach: I say
to the child, "This body of yours is the only house you will ever have
in which to live; only one body is given to a person. This body of
yours is part and parcel of all it has met since the beginning of time.
We can't change that at all, but we have to accept what we are when
we are born. Our color, size, our physical makeup . . . we can't
change any part of it. We did not pick our parents or our place to be
born. Now this body of yours can be a good place to live if you will
make yourself do what is best for it to develop to its maximum pos-
sibility. You and you alone can do that.

"This body will gain or lose as you feed it, and you alone can
control that. Your mother might deprive you of food, or I might put
you in the hospital where you could not get more food than I or-
dered for you; or I might give you a pill to ease your appetite or
prescribe exercise to the extent you would lose weight. There are
many ways to make you lose weight, but there is only one way to
do it right. I might say your mother is to blame because she nags
you all day about eating, or she cooks food you should not eat, or
she buys sweet drinks you should not have, or she lets you eat between meals, or she continues to say before you that she cannot
control you or your eating, or that all members of the family for

generations have been fat. We can tell you that you have some psychological disturbance that makes you eat.

"These are all very good excuses and with some people they might pass and give a good feeling that someone else is to blame for their being gluttons, and they will not have to suffer for that sin. But I say to you again, this is the only body you will ever have to live in; and you are the one to decide what is going into it. If you eat excessively and get fat and ugly, you still have to stay in your own body. If you eat and get fat and are always tired carrying this heavy load, perhaps you cannot have the fun other children have.

"I would not use your mother's nagging or your family history or the psychological factor as an excuse. You eat because you like the taste of food and you would rather eat than take care of this house you live in. So you must make up your own mind what you want in life, but remember that this body is your one and only home."

This has worked with children who are mentally able to think. The way to solve the problems of life is to show man that he has been endowed with the power to think and make decisions. God is willing to help us take this body, no matter how poor it was when given to us, and make it a blessing if we will only learn to discipline ourselves and say to ourselves, "If I take this road, I am willing to take all the bumps ahead and not blame them on man or God."

Children must be taught from birth that in man there is a trinity: a spirit to do good, a spirit to do bad, and himself as the solver. He is the only person who can decide which road to take.

I am sure Eli had taught his sons in the temple, and I am sure David knew he had no right to another man's wife. I am sure if we do anything to this body we have that will make it less efficient, we know it is wrong. But man still does wrong because he wants to do wrong. The wrong is what he wants more than right. We just have to come to ourselves and remember that man is a trinity and that we can't blame anyone else for our acts. When people come to us for help, we have to tell them the truth: that they behave as they do because they want to, and that they will have to take the blame and must pay for all their transgressions.

We know there are people that are deprived of the power of thinking due to some physical or chemical abnormality of the brain, perhaps born with mental defects so great they are not able to know right from wrong. These people have to be protected against themselves and other people. Then we have people who have lost their power of judgment through sickness or accidents. Also we have a group that have destroyed their power of judgment chemically through the use of drugs. These two groups of people, those that are physically and those that are chemically deprived of judgment, show no sign of a bodily conflict between good and evil and they never make excuses for their acts. These people that never feel or show guilt must be protected against man and self.

The man who feels guilt and feels the great conflict in his own body is the person who needs help. These are the people who make up a large percentage of the so-called sick adults and a portion of the sick children. No person can be happy if there is a war inside him. A mother neglecting her child will need a doctor for herself; wife neglecting her husband, her church, her God; father neglecting his job, his family, his church, his God, becomes sick. These conflicts in people are so evident that the very minute you start talking to them, they come up with an excuse to defend their acts. If you will give them a few words, they will convict themselves. We don't have to go back and dig into the dark past and try to find all kinds of unsightly closet skeletons to blame for our acts today.

Unless a human being is handicapped physically or chemically, the conflict, the great war is on in that mind and soul. When we are with a person for a short time and watch him act and hear him talk, we can spot the sin that is causing the conflict. His entire body is thrown into the battle and all conversation comes back to a dialogue of defense of the thing he is doing wrong, comes back to the conflict with arguments to defend his wrong.

Many teenagers come in for a check-up who are not sick but just unhappy and seem to have chips on their shoulders. They will say, "Mama is always after me about going to bed, my lessons, my eating, my dress. I get enough sleep and I should be permitted to eat what I please but she finds fault." These young people know they are wrong and that they are destroying their bodies that were bought with a price and they know they are torturing their parents. They are really sick. The conflict in a human soul throws every organ out of balance. Hate has made them sick. Envy is a killer. You will hear a boy say, "John gets all the good breaks at school; he is the teacher's pet." That boy can't learn, his mind is on something else besides learning, and his envy has made him sick. Then the statement that comes so many times, "I am not popular; the students don't like me." Jealousy is the downfall of so many. On and on it goes and the cure comes when the conflict is over, and it can never be over until right prevails.

There is never a fight in a human soul when that person comes out for right. Tension and torture lose their pain when we decide for right. Peace in the soul is the only happiness on earth, and each person only can bring that to pass.

The mind is never free to work as long as there is a raging battle inside and every living soul that is not demented knows what the conflict in his own soul is about. He does not have to go dig in the ruins of Pompeii to find some old skeletons to take the blame. In every living soul there are thousands of these old relics that could be unearthed but not one will really make us feel justified in our behavior and bring us happiness no matter how much we pay the archaeologist and how much he brings up. We ourselves are the judges, we are on trial, and all the alibis on earth cannot satisfy. They come up and we grab at each one as a sinking man at a straw, but they will not hold. We must swim if we are to be saved. We must say to ourselves, "Self, you are endowed with knowledge and wisdom; come out and strip off all your false attire, strip down to your soul, and find out where you stand." Let us look at ourselves, forget all the past, and know we are judged for today, that we are held responsible for our own acts. If we are to be well and happy, we must be willing to give up the things that are causing the conflict, always remembering that we cannot break the laws of God and be happy on this earth.

♂ ♀

11. Selecting a
way of life: career

One of the first questions asked a parent after a baby is born is, "What we you going to make out of this child?" Sometimes this question is asked to make conversation and sometimes it is asked in all sincerity. Sometimes the question is answered in jest and sometimes the question is answered, "I don't know; time will tell." This question was not asked so much years ago as it is now for a son was expected to carry on his father's trade or business and a girl would carry on the time-honored occupation of making a home and rearing other good men or women.

This situation has changed tremendously in the past fifty years. Each little boy and girl who comes into this world is privileged to make his or her own way of life. My father was a farmer and had six sons. Not one of his sons ever farmed a day after they were grown. We doctors still promise to train our children in the art of healing, but today the average doctor's sons or daughters do not study medicine.

Children come into the world today with many enticing roads to travel, with big signboards on every corner telling them how easy it is to get rich without working or how they can get something for nothing. The big question is: "In what way of life can I get the most security? Where can I get the most for the least?" The question should be: "How can I spend my life to be of the most help?" How can we use this short time we have on earth to give little children a better chance? How can it be used to make a better world? We must be taught from birth that we must first give and then we will always receive. So it is easy for children to become confused as to what they should do with their lives.

When a child is born, he is endowed with a certain amount of talent and ability, and it is my belief that there is a plan for his or her life. Each person has a certain number of brain cells and they have a certain innate ability; we cannot add one more to the lot and we cannot make them any better; but we can make them worse by not feeding and training them.

For example, a child that is born with cretinism may have the ability to be an A-plus student; but if he does not get thyroid, he will never learn to read. When a child is born, his size, his hearing, seeing, and every part of his body have all the possibilities stored up in that body, and it is the responsibility of the child's parents, the teacher, preacher, and all of those who make up his or her environment, to develop them. The challenge is to take this child as he is and the brain he has and develop both to greatest capacity.

The Downs Syndrome Child

Once we thought Downs Syndrome was a condition we could not do anything about. All these children looked alike and were put in the same class of people who could not be helped or trained, and the only thing to do was to hide them away and say, "I don't know why God did this to us, but I am sure it was for some good purpose." The parents lived a life of self-pity and were led to believe that there was no help for these people.

First, the parents must know the truth about the child they have. God did not make our child a Downs Syndrome Child any more than we broke our child's leg when he fell out of a tree. Something went wrong that was physical in the making of that child.

If a Swede married an American Indian and had a bronze-colored child, we would not say God made him that color. His color was the physical outcome of certain genes. Parents must be taught that there is a great deal that can be done with these children. They have always been of great interest to me, and in the past fifty years I have seen some of them develop into well-trained, pleasant and attractive people. They can be trained to obey, to be neat, and to do many routine jobs.

When a mother and father bring one of these babies to me, I always tell them the truth about his condition, but I never say to them, "You have a Mongolian Idiot on your hands and the quicker you get him out of your home before you learn to love him, the better it will be. You should put him in an institution or some home." No, in my opinion that would be bad advice to any mother and father.

In the first place, they will not learn to love this child too much to give him up when the time comes to put him in a special school or institution. Parents never love normal children too much to put them in such a school if it is to the advantage of the children to do so.

What they call love in the case of Downs Syndrome may well be pity, remorse, thinking, "We are being punished or disgraced with this child and deep down in our hearts we wish and pray that he could not live." So these normal thoughts make the parents build up a false pretense of great love to cover up their normal feeling of wanting the child not to live in this handicapped condition. If all this is explained to the parents, they see that what they were calling love was just pity, and the problem of being over-anxious about over-loving and one day giving the child up to go to a special school when the time comes is not a problem at all.

This thing we call conscience will run a mother and father crazy if they don't understand that every mother and father feels that way about a child that has no chance to grow up to be a normal person. They really pray that this little fellow may go if he can't have what they call a happy life and every sickness is met with a tormenting expectation that maybe the prayer will be answered this time. People should not be ashamed and condemn their feelings about this type of child. They could not help it, and they did not cause the condition. So they must face the facts, the problem is here, and there is no reason to be remorseful or ashamed.

After all, this little fellow will be easy to care for. This is my advice to the parents. A plan and feeding schedule are worked out for the child as carefully as for a normal child. He is kept on the abdomen to keep the head from becoming peak-topped, which used to be one of the cardinal signs of a Mongoloid. If left on their backs, the bone formation is slow and the head becomes very flat in the occipital region, which gives the head the peaked look.

The child is started on small doses of thyroid at birth and gradually increased to larger doses, sometimes as much as two grains. This increases metabolism; and the bone age can be maintained at a normal level with the right dose of thyroid. The hair that usually is thin, dry, and unruly can be beautiful and normal. The child will not have the customary fat, pot-bellied look, and the appetite will be good.

At six or seven months, I have the tonsils and adenoids removed. As these little children are built so close in the post nasal area, they have to breathe through the mouth as a rule and when the tonsils and adenoids are removed, they can breathe through the nose, keep their mouths closed, and not develop the thick, red, swollen, protruding dry tongue that is so unsightly. They are disciplined and punished as a normal child, and the mother and father are taught to feel like they have a job to do that is bigger than with a normal child, one they must do with love, not pity. These children are less trouble than normal children for the first two years and, if the parents send them off to a home or institution as soon as they are born, they spend a large amount of money that could well be used for schooling after the child is of school age. Almost all of these children live now since we have good drugs. Before the day of antibiotics, a parent was assured the child would not live more than four years because these children usually have colds from the time they are born. Their noses and throats are built small, the air passages are so small they can't breathe normally, and the sinuses cannot be kept open, so there is a constant infection.

By making their bodies as attractive as possible and giving them a mixed vaccine to make them build up immunity against respiratory infections, removing tonsils and adenoids, and disciplining, we can teach these children so that they can do for themselves and do for others. They cannot select a way of life or a career, but have to he trained as we would train any animal that does not have judgment. It is a big pay-off if parents can be persuaded to accept these little people and start at birth training them and being patient with their slow development.

This group of human beings is the only group that will not rebel against parental selection of a way of life. So-called normal human beings must be trained and taught from birth, but when it comes to the selection of the road they will take in life, each individual (if free) has to make this selection. This truth should be a constant reminder in the training of every human being if that person is to get the most out of life.

The Parent as the Teacher

Today we have all kinds of tests and scientific methods to help a person find the right road in life and I am sure they have been of great help at times and have influenced many people who had never been taught to make a decision for themselves. The tests show they are interested and are apt in some field, so they take that road thinking it will be easy, yet they may never be happy in the work they do. There is something in every person that tells him the road to take and many times that road means hard work, low pay, no fanfare, but, if followed, would bring happiness.

The best example of this is being a mother or teacher. Both of these jobs mean long hours and poor pay in money, but in the end the finished product brings more joy than any job on earth. So the tests may get us on the wrong road. We cannot take a road just because it is easy, for that road may not lead to where we were intended to go. This is the big difference between man and beast; man has knowledge and wisdom and the power of selection . . . each individual has to do this for himself. Just think what this world would be like if parents could select their children's way of life. There would be nobody to dig the ditches, scrub the floors, plough the soil; and I am afraid the world would be overrun with supervisors, presidents, doctors, lawyers, artists, opera singers, preachers, priests, and all the kinds that never have soiled hands.

Parents with abnormal children can select a way of life for them but parents with normal children must train them knowing that the children must be permitted to select their own way of life. Parents who have abnormal children of any type know from experience that a child is never so badly afflicted that he cannot be helped and trained to some extent. Such children should have all the training they are capable of taking but never forced beyond their capacity. Any mother and father can tell when a child is doing all he can do.

Each day is important in bringing a little child to find his place in life and, if we miss our chance to teach when he is ready to learn, we can't go back and get it. This is the big reason why a child needs his own parents all the time. A mother has important problems to solve every day from the day the baby is born until he goes out in life as a finished product. I heard a person say recently. "There is a tremendous waste of brain power by women." He was talking about building gadgets. I say the greatest job on earth is to build a man or woman and that is where the best female brain power can do the most good. Nobody can know like a pediatrician how much harm can be done by a sorry mother and how much good can be done by a good mother. We see that time and time again every day. We always get good fruit from good trees. And I am sure the same law holds with parents; sorry parents produce sorry children and good parents produce good children. A child's doctor can't help thinking at times that certain children are demon possessed, but we know that these children had to be taught good or bad.

When a child becomes old enough to understand, parents and friends begin to ask him the question, "What are you going to do when you are grown?" The answers are always along the line of what the child is most interested in at that time. In my day, if my brothers were asked what they would do when they were grown, the answers would have been: drive horses, farm, or keep store, as horses, farm, and country store were the interests my father had and as little boys, they were fascinated with that life. Today a boy might say he wanted to be a space man, or truck driver, or airplane pilot, or many other similar jobs as the world has changed and many different ways of life have evolved. The answer a child may give may change every month or year, but in some cases the answer is the same from childhood to manhood.

A Child Must Select His Own Way

Some children seem to know from an early age what they want to do in life but with most people this matter of finding a place in the world is a process of evolution. At each stage the parents should show the child the good or bad that could come out of the way of life in which he says he is interested. As a child expresses a desire to be a doctor, lawyer, bank robber, et cetera, the parents have an excellent opportunity to teach the child right from wrong. Johnny may be asked what he is going to do when he is a man, and he may say he will be a doctor like Doctor Smith. That is a good time to teach him the real mission of a doctor: to make little children well, to help grandpa's sore leg, to bring little babies into the world. Just a few words at this time may make a lasting impression and the ambition stronger. He will learn that doctors are here to help, not hurt.

The child may say, "I want to be a bank robber and get lots of money." Then the important lesson of ownership of property can

come up and just a few words said may do a great deal in demon-
strating to the child that we can have only the things we work for. If
that expressed ambition were answered like this, it might have a
lasting impression on his little mind. Just say, "How would you like
for somebody to come in your good papa's store and take all his
money so that we would not have any food or home? Every time a
man robs some person who has worked for his money that person
has to do without." That one statement might be the changing of a
little boy's train of thinking that might be his downfall if not
changed. The time to teach a lesson is when the child shows an
interest. If that interest is in something that is good, show him just
how good it would be if he did that for a livelihood. If it is bad,
show him just how bad it would be if he decided to pursue that
course.

We can't be careful enough about the things we say in the presence
of children. A good example of this was demonstrated one afternoon
when my three-year-old nephew was visiting me. We were on the
terrace and a little bug crawled by and Billy said, "Aunt Leila, I am
going to kill that bug," and I said, "Billy, you wouldn't kill a poor
little bug that is going out to get food for his little children. Tonight
when mama bug gets supper ready and the little children ask where
papa bug is and mama bug has to tell them little Billy killed their
father, that would be bad." He did not kill the bug and some months
later while he was visiting his grandmother in Savannah, Georgia,
she saw a fly in the kitchen and asked Billy to bring her the fly swat-
ter so she could kill the fly. Billy said, "Grandmother, you would not
kill a poor little fly, would you? That little fly has children back
home." That statement I made on the terrace was forgotten by me,
but in the mind of that three-year-old it lasted.

The evolution of a career is interesting to study. If we adults will
think back, we will see how one desire after another appeared and
how they were handled. Some were heart breakers and some were
joy makers. In it all we had a feeling of being drawn to a certain goal
and, if we got off on a tangent because a particular course seemed to
be easy or more profitable, we still felt that forceful urge tugging at
us and it would not let go. When we want to do a thing but we are
not willing to do it because of the work, or because we are unwilling
to give up the easy road, we cannot be happy.

I have a friend whose father was a very successful businessman
who had built up a profitable business and this young man would be

the person to carry on the business. This was talked and planned but from the time this boy could say what he wanted to do, his desire was to be a doctor. His father was wealthy, and there was no reason for this boy to have to work for a living. The study of medicine was long and hard, so he was discouraged by everybody that knew him. He got married and had children, but he could not get away from that compelling desire to be a doctor. One day his mother said to me, "My son will never be happy until he is a doctor. What do you think about his going back to school this late in life to learn a profession that takes so much time and hard work?" The next time I saw her she said he had left for school. That man has become one of the finest, kindest doctors I know, and he works like a man who has one objective in life, to fill his rightful place in society.

I believe each one of us has a place in this world and that we can reach our goal if we will do every step in the climb the best we can and see the opportunities as they appear and take advantage of them. I am sure some people fail to reach their goal because they do things that hold them back. They are not willing to pay the price or do the work or do without. They refuse to see what they really see. They close their eyes for fear they will see the road that will mean hard work and long hours. They go through life expecting the things they want to be handed to them. That is not the way this universe was planned. It was planned that man should work six days out of seven. He has eyes to see and should see, has a mind to think and should think out for himself a route to his goal. A person may be born physically blind, deaf, or may not have legs, but whatever he has he should feed, develop, and keep free of anything that would prevent the body he has from functioning to its fullest capacity.

We cannot reach our goal in life if our minds and bodies are disturbed by constant stimulation and depression that we get from alcohol, tobacco, caffeine, barbiturates, tranquilizers, or any drug that with constant use will lower the level of normal stimulation of the physiological or psychological responses. To see great minds that can't come to the surface until they are stimulated by alcohol or tobacco is bad because the use of the substance gradually lowers the base and more and more is needed to make the mind act. It is tragic to think of all the great minds that are dulled long before they would have been by age, minds that might have found a cure for cancer, written a better book, or made a better child.

As we search for our place in life there is something that is always telling us what we should do and where we could be of the most value to this world. We must be willing to look for it and work for it and no person is ever truly happy until he fills the niche in life he wants to fill. If he fails, he knows it is his own fault although he may try to think up excuses and reasons for placing the blame on something or somebody. The lack of money is over-worked. I could never believe a person missed his goal in life because of the lack of money, knowing that I started to medical college with only sixty-two dollars.

Aversion to work has been the thing that has stopped the greatest number short of happiness. Parents may be blamed for not being interested enough to supply the force and the money but that excuse is no good. With an interest in work and the ability to make a decision, the lack of money excuse is never used.

One excuse is, "I got married." Now that excuse is not good either. If a husband or wife is not willing to help the other reach a goal, marriage should have been left off until the goal was reached. Certainly we don't have laws to force people to get married. Another excuse that is used by some is that they were born on the wrong side of the tracks. In the United States that is the poorest of all excuses for, if a person wants to rise to success, the question is not asked, "From what class are you?" There are thousands of excuses stored up for those who want to use them, but they are no good. They may make a person feel better for a while, but inside him as long as he lives is a recognition of unfinished business that he continues to worry about.

Children should be taught and encouraged to ask the reason for things and they should be given concise, definite answers; and each question should be answered when the interest is there.

After I examine a child's throat, I always give him the tongue depressor and it is interesting to see the different reactions. Some are so angry they throw it down or will not take it at all, some take it, break it in half, and throw it down on the floor, while others will ask for the second tongue depressor to make an airplane. Still another will take it and give it to mother to take home. Some will say, "Thank you." This shows the kind of training they have had and how they react to help. As a rule, these children will react to help and advice the same way through life.

Some children break their toys in a temper and mama will say, "Now don't cry; I will buy you another one." That child is not likely to ever take care of anything, for he is taught that he can destroy and yet have, which is not true. When he gets out on his own and mama is not there to replace the things he destroys, he will have to learn this lesson the hard way. The mother should say to the child when he breaks a toy in a fit of temper or just destroys a toy or a tongue depressor, "Son, tomorrow you will want that tongue depressor to make an airplane or that toy truck to build a road, and you won't have it; and I am not able to get you another." This is an important lesson to teach and practice early if a boy or girl is to reach any kind of goal. Destruction and extravagance are the forerunners of a great many of the heartaches a parent has to face. For a person to succeed he must learn the value of money, how it is made, how it should be spent; and if this lesson is learned early, the over-worked excuse of not being financially able to do the thing he knows he should do is not used.

Every answer to a question should carry a reason if a child is to develop and find his place in life. I had one mother who always had the same answer to all her child's questions. The answer was always "Because." That child developed the habit of asking the question and always ending with "Because." He answered his own question since "Because" seemed to be the answer to all questions.

As a child grows older and begins to have a genuine interest in art, music, law, farming, medicine, teaching, or thousands of other ways of life, the parents should encourage each of these interests. The interest may be for a day or it may be for a lifetime. The parents should not overemphasize the interest with too much talk or force, but should let it work out gradually. Too much interest on the parents' part has killed off many promising careers. It is best to let the child want the career or way of life and be willing to sacrifice to get it.

From two years of age to the grave, a human being that is really alive likes a challenge and things that come easy don't seem very important. If a boy has to cut the neighbor's lawn to get money to take piano lessons, he will practice; if he has to carry a paper route to earn money to buy a microscope, he will take care of it and use it. So these interests that come may be for a day and the horse we buy may never be ridden or the piano may never be played. However, we must expose children to these varied interests and try to be sure there is an interest before we overplay it and disgust them with our overinterest. We must do our best to make them want these things. A career should be a privilege, not a task.

The question is asked every day by young people, "How can I know what I want to do with my life?" There is only one answer, that is, that they do the things they are doing the best they can and follow their greatest interest, always saying to themselves, "Will this interest be an honor to my parents, my country, and my God?" If not, they should try to find an interest that will honor parents, country, and God for there cannot be lasting happiness in a career that falls below that standard no matter how much it provides in this world's goods. If a career runs counter to the physical, chemical, or moral laws, it will not bring happiness.

The happiest people are not necessarily those who have made the most money, or made the headlines in the news, but they are those who have done the best they could with what they had in an effort to make a better world. I think it is a sin not to make money, for money is one of the rewards for work; and it is a sin not to work. At the same time a person is not judged in the sight of God by the amount of money he has made, but by how he made it and how he spent it. There is no known career on earth that is not honorable if it pleases man, country, and God. This is a great lesson to teach our children. If they can't climb to the top of the highest mountain, they should do the best they can; and to climb to the top of a hill, if it is the best they can do, is just as honorable in the sight of the Great Judge.

My daughter said to me one day, "Mama, I don't know what I want to do. I am all confused. You always knew you wanted to be a doctor." No, as a child I did not know a woman could become a doctor but I loved to see things live. I would pick up flowers that had been thrown out as dead and put them in water and see them come back to life. I would help a little sick chicken, or get a grasshopper out of a spider web, or help my father doctor a sick cow. I would make salve for the sores on my little brothers and sisters and the little colored children on the farm. I would hang on the lot fence for hours watching a sick horse, or would pick up worms in the road to keep them from being killed by the traffic, always trying to save life, from the smallest plant to the largest animal.

My family and my friends were sure I would be a milliner and make hats, for that was what I seemed to do best, make doll hats and dress hats for all the family. I also liked to sew, and dressmaking seemed to be a natural interest. Each year my interest changed, but the desire to make creatures and things live and to know why they had to be sick and die was my greatest interest and one that never changed.

Through grammar school, high school, and college the study of animals, man, chemistry, and physics was a great joy, but the study of music and language was a task. In college a great teacher, Dr. Macon, had the same interest so he let me set up a little private anatomy laboratory where I could study these things out myself. It was then I acquired the nickname "Doc," with no idea of becoming a doctor as there was no school in the South that would admit a woman to the study of medicine at that time. I thought teaching would be the only thing I could do. In that little laboratory I learned a great deal.

I finished college and tried teaching for two years, but that was not my field. I sent my application in to medical college, but it was not acknowledged. The day for medical school to open I was there and asked to be admitted but was refused on the grounds that the school had fifty-two students already and there was room for only thirty-six so it would be out of the question for me to get a place. I asked them to just fix me a place in any corner and take me on a trial basis for a few days. So the officials of the school got together that night and decided to let me stay. They had one married man and one Yankee boy nobody wanted to work with so they put us three outcasts together. (This was a Southern college.) A married man in school at that time was not at all popular and a Yankee less so, and even less than that, a female student.

We three started on a cadaver and became good friends, had great fun and soon we were taken in by the entire class. My four years there passed like a day because I was doing the thing I wanted to do.

We should not worry about our child not having a fixed goal but should help him to see that what he does today is important, whether it is cutting the grass or baking a cake, and that he should do each job well and follow his greatest interest remembering that the only way to win is by working.

From the poorest developed human being mentally and physically to the most perfectly developed, all have to find a place in the social and economic climate in which they live. So they should be fitted into the little niche that is fit for them. This can never be done until parents are willing to recognize their children's ability and not try to make out of them what they, the parents, would have liked their lives to be.

The state requires children to go to school until they are sixteen, which makes our country sound very intellectual. But society should let the children who are not capable of taking an education know that even though they have been through high school, it is no disgrace to make a living with their hands and that college training is not something every person must have to be a success. A person who is capable of learning should go as far as possible and use the gift of a good mind to help his fellow man to see and enjoy the glorious gifts that this world holds for those who will only work. We can't say enough, we can't live the example of work enough to show our children the value and the happiness that come from work. With the idle rich or the idle poor, the evening brings unrest and regrets, but a day spent in honest work brings happiness and a good night's sleep.

The Importance of Work

One thing that is so wrong, and I think sinful, is our present-day feeling about work. If we see a woman washing her clothes in a stream or a man ploughing with a mule, we pity them because they are working hard. This is wrong; if that is the best they can do, they will get as good a night's sleep from their work as one would from working on Telstar. We must teach our children that no matter how small the job is, if it is to help to make a better world, it is good. The man who digs a ditch and digs it well gets the same reward for his day's work as the man who builds a good idea. A mother who has worked hard all day building a child gets as great a reward as the nurse on a battlefield who helps to save a life.

When a child talks about what he wants to do in life, if the goal is not something that would be dishonorable, he should never be discouraged even though we think he is not strong enough physically or mentally to reach that goal. I hear this statement, "Oh, you can't do that; it is for somebody with money or position." Finding our place in life is somewhat like mountain climbing; we arrive at the foot of the mountain and one person will say, "Oh, you'd better not try that; the trail is too steep, the rocks are too big, the trail is wet, you can't make it." Then we meet another person and he will say, "Oh, don't miss that trip; the view up there is heavenly; it is steep but you can make it; there are some rocks but you can go around

them, and the dampness on the trail makes walking easy." Now watch
the reactions of the people. Some will go back to their cars and never
try. Others will start and make out well for a while and get the pleasure of viewing as long as they are able to climb, seeing things they
would never have seen if they had not tried, and when they find
they cannot make the top and they have gone as far as they can go,
they look over the beautiful world and say, "Thank the Heavenly
Father for the strength that brought me this far and bless those who
are able to go on to the top."

Then there are the ones who make the top and who received the
same advice at the bottom as the others. Their prayer should be like
this, "Thank the Heavenly Father for the strength and faith that
brought me to the top and bless my fellow travelers who tried and
did not make it, for their reward is as great as mine; they did the
best they could." This is our child's life; he may start out to be a
doctor and end up waiting tables. We should never be one to say, "I
told you you could not make it" nor say to our child, "Don't try that
for it is too hard." We should not be the person to discourage them
and cause them to go get in their cars and drive away never knowing
what that trail was like. If they can't do it, they get a great pleasure
out of knowing they tried, and maybe when they got to that first
lookout on the trail and could not go any further, they realized this
was really what they wanted in life anyway.

We hear this every day, "My son started out to be a doctor and we
were disappointed in him for he is just teaching school. My daughter
started out to be a teacher and all she has done was to get married
and have a family." Let us encourage our child to try the trail and if
he stops at some lookout and never gets any higher and this is the
best he can do, we must never make him feel that we think he has
failed and should teach him not to envy the fellow traveler that made
the top. That is one of the hardest lessons on earth to learn. To see
the fellow on the top of the mountain knowing that he is able to see
in every direction and here we are on a lookout and can see in only
one direction! It is hard to say, "Thank God he made it and thank
God I got as far as I did and did not turn back at the foot of the
mountain."

Ambition is one thing, but the right road may be another, for if
our ambition makes us take one step that is not just to our fellow
man, the end results will not be happiness. If we cheat in order to

be valedictorian of our class, every congratulation cuts like a knife. If we court the boss and get the job our fellow worker should have had, the sight of that man makes us hate ourselves. We should teach a child to be ambitious, but use the same amount of time teaching him to be just. Ambition, envy, and justice are three factors that break or make men. Ambition is a great thing, but we must teach our children by word and example that if there is someone on the trail that can hike faster than they can, they must step aside and let him pass and bid him God's speed.

Envy is a killer, a heartbreaker, a gastric ulcer, a mind destroyer, a ball and chain; it is everything that is wrong. Justice is the Balm in Gilead. One day I asked a little boy what he wanted to be when he became a man. He said, "I want to be a millionaire." Money-making would not be a bad career, if the ambition did not destroy justice. The desire to make money should never be great enough to make a man destroy or injure his fellow man and we should so teach our children.

Many boys and girls are talked into college or forced to go when they are not mentally able to make the grade and they have to suffer the embarrassment of flunking out and being sent home. Now if the child wanted to go and was willing to make the effort and it turned out he couldn't make the grade, the embarrassment would not be as great since he was not forced into it by his parents. If a horse has more than he can pull and his master applies the whip, the horse goes up on his hind feet and may wreck the wagon or he may try and just stand still. This is so true of a human life. Man knows how much he can do and, if he is forced by stimulants or drugs beyond that, there may be a wreck. If we are trying to fit into a niche that is too big or too small, we are never happy. Thousands of wasted dollars have been spent trying to make a violinist out of a good truck driver.

Parents should, if they are able, give their children a chance at every worthy desire. When they have tried and it is clear they cannot do it, or that they are not interested, they should be permitted to quit.

If we plan our child's life and talk it all the time when the child is not capable or is not interested in the life we plan, the child always feels his parents think he is a failure.

We must not say that our child will be a doctor, lawyer, preacher, or follow any other specific career. If we have a desire for his life, we should expose him to this career as much as possible and do no talking about what we are going to do with his life, but always talk about what he is going to do with his own life. Let's give our child a chance by example, not by force.

♂ ♀

12. Dissipation

My first school was a two-room schoolhouse. We knew all the children in that school and their parents. We knew their family background. My great-great-grandfather had obtained the original land grant for a large portion of that county, and it was easy to trace the family history of most of these children.

In that school were three families: one had five children; one, seven; and one, four. Their parents were well-to-do farm owners. The children had good clothes and good food. They went to church and their environment was as good as the average child's in that school. But children of these families just could not make the grade. If there was any trouble in the school or the community, it seemed to go back to one of these families. Not one of these children finished high school. They were restless and had tempers they could not control. They were devoid of ambition and were unable to concentrate long enough on anything to make satisfactory progress. In school they were the type who could not stay in their seats or control their talking. It seemed impossible for them to control their behavior and at times they would just shake their hands and dance around.

After leaving that school and entering college, I worked regularly in a cotton mill village mission. Here was a group of children that could not compete with the children of the small college town and there was a school for them in the mill village. These children showed no evidence of desiring an education. They lacked creative interest and were not concerned with making their lives better, but seemed to be willing to go on as their parents always had. We worked in the homes as well as in the church with these people. They had good clothes, their homes were warm and well built, their food was simple but adequate. But there was as much difference between the children of this mill village and the other children of the small college town as between children living in different sections of the country or even in different countries.

These mill village children could not possibly have kept up with the children in the college town. As I taught Sunday School four years in the little church in the village, I had ample opportunity to study the reactions of these children and their lack of ambition. The boys were troublemakers. If anything went amiss in the town, it seemed always to be traced back to these boys. The picture was this: a big boy, two or three grades behind his age group, who just couldn't fit into society, like the problem boys in my first school.

There was not much worry or talk about girls in that day. Girls generally just followed a pattern in the mill village. There was no worry if they did or did not go to school. As soon as they were grown they would get married and have a family. Thus little was said about girls who could not learn. They got married the day they changed from a little girl to a woman and had another family like the ones from which they came. After marriage a girl dressed, talked, thought, cooked, ate, and dipped snuff like her mother. The day she got married she put on a long dress, put her hair in a knot on top of her head, and wore an apron with a pocket to carry her snuff and dip stick. Yes, they were a society of people so different from the people across the road one could never believe they were of the same race. No matter how hard one worked with them, their way of life could not be changed. Four years' work in that village seemed to be wasted time. College girls had worked with these people twenty-five years or more before I started, and they could not make any headway. These were people with thick, yellow, "cobblestone" skin, hair that was dry and unruly, thin bodies, poor posture, poor appetite, slick tongues, sad faces, no ambition, no desire to be any better.

At that time the social workers thought environment was responsible. Give these people better food, better houses, better recreation, better religious training, and the problem would be solved, they said. Good food is essential, also a comfortable place to live, a place to play and a place to worship; but, if the mind is not receptive and capable, these side helps cannot change a person's way of life.

After finishing college, I taught in a town that had a nearby mill village. So I continued this study. The work we did seemed almost futile. There was no desire or ambition on the part of these children to better themselves. They would accept our help but never wanted to help themselves, just would not think, and were perfectly satisfied to duplicate their parents' pattern of life. From among these people in that day came many of the so-called "bad" boys. The question continued in my mind: why can't these children think, or why won't they think? Why can't they come out of this kind of life and add something to the world? Why can't this sad, whipped, undernourished look be changed into one of happiness?

After finishing medical college, I started working in a big medical mission run by Central Presbyterian Church in Atlanta. In that mission were all types of people and poverty. In that clinic I could study people who seemed to be in a perpetual state of poverty as well as those reduced to poverty by some mishap. Here was all the material one could want to make a study of developmental differences in children. Many of the children were from the slum areas, pale, dirty, sad expressions on their faces, no desire for cleanliness or improvement, accepting the help of others, never saying, "Thank you."

After more than fifty years of working with these people, I have seen like produce like, and poverty is not the cause. Here, for example, is a case that is rather typical of those that have been repeated time and time again among the families of this medical mission. A mother with four boys had lost her husband and was on welfare, without money to buy good food in the amount and type they needed, or good clothes. This family had to live in what was called the slums. All four of these boys grew to be fine men with college educations. Yet many others repeated the patterns of the families in the community where I first attended school, and the patterns of the typical mill village families, where I attended college and first taught school, producing children who could not or would not rise out of the circumstances in which they lived.

Why did some make the grade while others did not? The cause was not differences in money, houses, food, clothing, recreation or exposure to the church. It was something much deeper.

Among the many possible factors, there was only one that was common to the three groups of people studied. Among the families of the first school in my home community, the families of the mill villages, and the families of the medical mission, one thing seemed to be consistently present among the poorer types described here.

The mothers of these children used great quantities of tobacco. The mothers in the farming community and in the mill villages used large amounts of snuff, most of them since they were children, and the mothers of the Central Presbyterian Church medical mission smoked, chewed, or dipped snuff. The mothers in these families smoked, chewed, or dipped tobacco for nine months before the children were born and, in some cases, where the mothers were upset, they used more tobacco during pregnancy than any other time.

It is a scientific, proven fact that everything a mother takes into the body while pregnant, the baby also gets. I have given mothers whooping cough vaccine and, when their babies were born, they had as many antibodies in their blood as their mothers. There is not one atom in the baby that did not come by way of the mother except the sperm that was united to the ovum that made the first cell. After that, what the mother ate, drank, or absorbed through the skin or lungs made the baby; and nature is not able to separate the good from the bad.

One could never believe that the baby who has been forced to smoke, chew, or dip tobacco from the time it was two microscopic cells until it was nine months old could be the baby that it would have been without this nicotine. Nicotine is classed with cyanide in the pharmacopoeia, yet thousands of babies are forced to consume this toxic drug at the most important time of life.

When I was a child, I lived on a farm in South Georgia. I went to a little country church, and there was a dividing line that ran down the middle of this church. It was as if a board ran down the middle aisle. Men sat to the right of the preacher and women and children to the left. If there was any speaking out to be done, the men did it; no woman would have been common enough to have expressed herself in that church. But you can be sure that never a man spoke that his wife did not know what he was going to say.

My father was the head of our house. But my mother was the neck, and the neck was the thing that turned the head. Men apparently ran that county, but at that time women were exercising their greatest constructive influence. Men respected women. Men tipped their hats to a woman, helped her in and out of a carriage or phaeton, opened and closed doors and gates, and offered her a seat when she entered a room. Women were queens in their homes in those days. No man would tell an off-color story, or use profane language before a lady. Women had a tremendous influence in the home, and, although they were not heard in public, they were the secret influence that made or destroyed the home.

During my childhood a railroad was built through our community and the town of Portal, Georgia, came into being on my father's farm. My father was elected mayor of the town, a position he held until his death some twenty-five years later. Many of the farmers in the community built homes in Portal. Stores, churches, and a school went up. Soon it was a busy little South Georgia town. Good farm land and the growing of cotton made it prosperous, and on the water tank in the middle of the town was the motto, "Watch us Grow."

One day my father came home with two tickets to a tent show that was to be there just one night. He did not ask my mother to go with him to a show in a tent and at night. Women just did not do those things and, too, my mother had little children and a good mother wouldn't have thought of leaving her children at night. So, as I was ten years old, I was not old enough to be disgraced by going with my father to a performance of that type. That was a great night. I am sure it was the first night I had been out to anything, for there was never any place to go at night except to visit a neighbor.

To me, that was a big tent. There must have been a hundred seats, all filled with men, boys, and a few girls my age or younger. The show went on. The man in charge announced the program, "Our show tonight is 'Ten Nights in a Bar Room.'"

There was never such drama put on the stage! By the time the show was over everybody inside the tent was in tears. My big, two hundred twenty-five pound papa had tears rolling down his tanned cheeks. I did not go prepared to cry so I had to use my petticoat to wipe away the tears.

Children of that day were not subjected to all the sob stories, crime, and tragedy that they are today, and this play made a big impression. I had never really known of but one serious crime in our part of the country, and that was when two men robbed and murdered our cousins, the Hodges family some eight miles away. The papers did not carry pages of stories about crime, and there was no misery and unhappiness coming into the home all day over radio or television. So that show with all its tragedy fell on virgin soil and made a great impression.

Suddenly, the show was over, the stage was cleared, the lanterns were turned up and out came a tall, pompous lady dressed in a black silk voile skirt over a taffeta petticoat, a white blouse with a high collar, watch on one shoulder, and glasses on the other. She really looked important, a woman making a speech in that tent full of men. You could hear the taffeta swish before you could see her. That was music to my ears, as I had an old maid cousin who had a skirt like that and one of my desires was to have an outfit like it when I was old enough. She was the most important-looking woman I had ever seen. As she walked on the stage, everybody tried to dry his eyes.

Three statements she made that night made a lasting impression on my mind. They went something like this:

"You people see what has happened here tonight. You are sad and I am sad, but this kind of conduct in our country is not necessary and should not be allowed. When the women of this country are permitted to vote with the good men of this country, we can stop all this tragedy."

The second point she made was, "When the women in these United States of America are permitted to vote with the good men of these United States, we can clean up politics."

The third point was, "When the women of this country are permitted to vote with the good men of this country, we can stop the tobacco habit that is getting a good hold on our young boys. You see all these young boys smoking these 'coffin tacks'? It stunts their growth and injures their mental and physical development."

As a child, these statements sounded good to me, and in my childish mind I felt that the whole country should fall in and do its part to give every little child a chance. The little I had known about the effects of alcohol on a good man in our little town had made me wish for some way to stop that tragedy. I did not know anything about politics, but if she said it needed to be made better, she was probably right as she looked like a person who knew what she was talking about. So I was all for making politics better. The so-called bad boys in our community had started the tobacco habit by smoking cigarettes, and I was sure that was not for the best. I left that show with a great dream of a better United States of America, and I am sure that suffragette was just as sincere in what she was talking about as any reformer who ever lived.

Women should be free to vote, for women were and always have been the force behind the men. They have made and trained every man on earth except Adam. As women think and conduct their lives, so goes the country, whether the women have freedom to vote or not. It would be impossible for a country to fail if every woman in that country did a perfect job in the making and training of boys and girls.

If the women like my mother would go out and have a part in the law-making of this country, it would have to be a better world. But it did not occur to me as a child that women had made the men who, for their own selfish gains, made a living destroying the only body a man or woman has; or that man would make and sell something that would destroy another man, woman, or child; or that men would make laws that would permit a man to kill his neighbor or his own child indirectly. All the evil in the world has to be made or sponsored by man. Man is made by woman; therefore, this suffragette really had a vision of what this country could be if all the women would do their part.

Woman suffrage sounded like a good idea. Some men and women were afraid of the idea, and there was a great fight. One of the strongest arguments against it was that a woman's place was in the home. There must be a foundation for any nation, and woman has always been that. If she left the home, the foundation would crumble and the country would go down. Another argument was that a home without a mother is not a home. We must not kill the goose that lays the golden eggs. When the trainer quits, we lose the race.

Yet in spite of all these arguments, women did win the right to vote which was proper, since women should have the right to vote and to be free to do the things they want to on an equal basis with men. But with all of these rights, woman must still be a woman and live the life of a woman and be the maker of men; for there is no other way on earth to make men. With freedom must come knowledge and wisdom and woman must know that freedom does not make her a man, that her body is the only source of man, and that man cannot be better than the material of which he is made. Woman was made by God as an instrument to produce man and she is the only source. Through her every man has had to come—blessed or cursed by her will to do good or evil in the making of that little body and in teaching him a way of life.

That suffragette was fighting a battle she was sure to win, but I wonder what she would now think her victory has meant in true value to little children. Women were queens in their so-called slavery and they ran the country but did not know it. Each home was a kingdom of its own and out of that kingdom came the great mothers and fathers, and out of that kingdom on the side of the hill or the flat lands came the great leaders of our country.

The mother of that day was the doctor. She did all the doctoring unless there was an operation needed. The doctor was called in if the fever lasted too long or if there were convulsions, and most mothers could do as much for the sick as the doctor could. They thought their problems through and in some way just knew what to do.

Mothers were lawyers and law makers. They set the standards in the home, and out of these homes came people with a conviction of right and wrong. They were for or against. The mother had time to teach her children fair play, and the father was the head of the home who spoke with authority to help her carry out her teaching.

Our home was run on this plan. Mother had twelve children and she was never too busy to help them. We always had supper before dark, after the outside jobs were finished. Then the dishes were washed and the children were gathered around the dining table with their books. Each child prepared the lesson for the next day at school. There was never any trying to get us down to work. My mother would just say, "Children, it is time to get your lessons for tomorrow."

There was nothing to interfere, no telephone, television, radio, or neighbors. It was dark outside, and the only light in the house during the lesson-getting period was on the dining room table. Mother would start with the youngest and go up the line. She would hear all the lessons in this order. When the last and oldest had gone to bed, she had assurance that each child could spell the assignment for the next day and read every line, parse every sentence, work every problem, answer all the geography questions. She knew that one teacher with forty or fifty children could not do more than hear their lessons and, if we were to get an education, she had to help. I can remember when we would have one of those long partial payment problems and not get the right answer. The next morning at breakfast mother would say, "Go look at that problem where we multiplied the fourth time and you will find your mistake."

I never saw her impatient with us. She had great dreams of making out of her children better doctors, lawyers, teachers, or world builders than she was. She was starting in the center of things to make a better world rather than trying, as we are today, to start from the outer edge, which is impossible.

The tent show and the suffragette talk more than seventy years ago was one approach to the problem of giving the child a chance. I just wonder what the suffragette would have to say if she were a pediatrician in 1982. I wonder what she would have to say about the fulfillment of her prophecy. For over sixty years we women have had the vote.

Women are engaged in every type of business, every profession, and they go as far as they please. We have them in the United Nations; in Congress; in medicine, law, diplomatic service; as heads of schools, bar tenders, cab drivers. Name the job and she is there. Women have conquered a man's world, and have the right to do anything a man does. No one would dare question that.

In history there has been one thing that always comes true. The army of occupation, if it stays long enough, is absorbed by the people it has conquered. I wonder if that is not true in this case. The great evils we were going to destroy and force out of the greatest nation on earth have played a reverse game, and have not only continued to destroy men by the thousands but have engulfed the only hope of a nation, the greatest of all fighters, the women. Has our emancipation brought man up to a higher level of right living and better health, or has woman lowered her standards and lost all she has been fighting for? Has the emancipation of women really made a happier world for little children? Have women used this great blessing of freedom to give little children a better chance of health and happiness?

A Woman's Greatest Responsibility

There are three things that should be of the utmost importance to a woman: first, what God thinks of her; second, what man thinks of her; and, finally, what children think of her. I wonder if in the past fifty years we have raised our standards in the sight of God, man, and our children! Has our conduct increased respect and reverence for women!

It is hard to believe that a woman or man could be selfish enough to destroy a child's chance yet we see evidence of this every day. A mother will bring in a little baby, his body stiff, his feet cold, spitting up his food, crying out with pain every time he is moved, with diarrhoea, or constipation. This baby is the result of two people who did not care enough to give him a chance. The mother made this baby smoke, drink, do without the proper food for nine months of pregnancy. Papa did not care enough about him to keep his own body in as good health as possible. He drank, smoked, and did not eat a balanced diet, did not give his body proper exercise or proper amount of rest. The sperm that fertilized the ovum that made this little body was no better than the body that produced it. Women could control this if they loved their offspring as much as they should. A woman in America has the right not to marry a man if she thinks he does not have the will to make his body perfect enough to be the father of her child.

We just don't think enough about the importance of building human beings. It is no different from the breeding of other animals or plants. We know we must first have good seed if we are to hope to grow good corn, and we know that this seed must have the right food, good soil, and moisture if it is to grow. This is true also if we hope to develop a normal human being.

Every girl should be taught from the time she can learn that the purpose of her body is to bring forth another body and it should be more perfect than her own, for she has the knowledge of the past. When I was a young girl, it was generally thought that all the bad boys and girls came from across the tracks. But that is not true today. A psychiatrist made a statement recently to the effect that more children classed as juvenile delinquents were being born to professional women than to any other known group of people.

It is hard to believe that such a statement could be true. But if we think this thing through, we will see that the professional women have gone into a man's world in a big way. They were the first women in the so-called better class to start dissipating. It was not true of all professional women, but those who did were bold enough to go all the way and really do a thorough job, not only smoking and drinking and carrying a cup of black coffee all day, but really showing the world they would not be bound down just because they had been born female.

Having to carry on their work in the role of both man and woman some of them, I am sure, had to have something to quiet their nerves after a long, busy day such as a professional woman of this type must have. A woman who tries to have a family life and a professional life at the same time is tackling a job that has always been big enough to require two people to do it well. So it is easy to see the psychiatrist may be right. A child that is born to a woman who has consumed great quantities of alcohol, caffeine, nicotine, and sleeping pills, who has had two jobs and not time enough to eat a balanced diet, could be a very upset individual. I am sure one could not expect a normal child out of that background.

I recall an interesting example of this. A prominent banker had been born well and married a girl of the same type. Both were college graduates and both professional people. After they became able to afford it, they started dissipating. The wife went all the way. They had two sons, neither of whom did well in school, but both did get through high school and tried college. These boys just could not adjust so their method of escape was alcohol. They could not live up to the record their parents had made in school and their parents could not accept sons who were not capable of doing as they had done.

So a great conflict developed in that home. The two sons became alcoholics. The only way they could make themselves feel important was to be under the influence of alcohol. The mother of these boys had made them smoke, drink alcohol, take great quantities of coffee and sleeping pills for nine months before they were born and she should have been willing to accept them as they were and not demand of them more than they were able to do. If she had done so, they would not have had to seek a way of escape.

After many years in the practice of medicine, I have seen a great change in the problems that come to doctors. The tears that were shed for little children forty or fifty years ago were brought on principally by the ravages of disease-causing organisms that killed or left the children handicapped. Medical science has made great progress in conquering and reducing disease but the mothers still come with their tears. Now they are shed over the child who is a product of dissipation, born to parents who did not care enough to give the child the best possible prenatal start, and then the best possible environment that would make for as perfect a life as possible.

Parents not willing to accept the child they make are the curse of the modern child.

Two generations ago what was called the better class of women would not think of dissipating during pregnancy. Now great numbers of pregnant women are chain smokers and alcohol addicts.

Little babies from the dissipated mother and father are brought into my office and this is about what I find, First, a nervous, upset mother and father who feel that they have been dealt a very unjust blow to have had a baby that has not been any pleasure, that has made them lose sleep, and that has made a complete wreck out of them.

"Doctor, this baby has wrecked us!"

At this point it breaks my heart to think that they put the blame on this little baby they created, not willing to say, "Doctor, we have wrecked a child's life, and will you help us to take what we have and make the best of it?" No, I have never heard the parent take the blame. It is always the child who is running them crazy and yet that child was made and trained by them. When we see these babies, we know there must be some way these parents will have to pay for this worst of all crimes, destroying the chance of a little child.

When the mother and father enter the office, the baby is always crying. She puts him down on the table as if she would just like to walk out and leave the thing that has caused her so much trouble. Then I get the history and it is always the same, "Doctor, I did not know the things that went into my body would go into my baby. My doctor should have told me."

Then if I look her right in the eyes and say, "Now, Mother, tell me the truth and put the blame in the right place," she will always say, "Sure, Doctor, I knew it was wrong."

On physical examination the first thing you see is a baby that seems to be in pain. When I stand him up, he is so stiff he can almost stand alone and every muscle is hard, seeming to be in tonic contraction. The expression on the face is one of great fear and pain. When you hold this baby, he pulls back and stiffens up and will not cuddle and fall to the body like a normal baby. (A normal baby, for the first three months, is so cuddly and relaxed he is like a little kitten when picked up.) The reflexes are exaggerated to the point that the legs, arms, and chin go into a convulsive state when disturbed. The feet and hands are cold, wet, blue, and the cry is loud and shrill. The baby jumps at the slightest noise or motion. As a rule, he is spitting up his milk and nothing seems to stay down, not even water. He seems to be nauseated.

The Problems of a Child of a Dissipated Mother

Of all the sad sights in medicine, this is the worst: a child born with a normal body, but wrecked by the dissipation of the mother who did not care or, I should say, who was selfish enough to make a little baby suffer the tortures of the damned.

When I first started the practice of medicine, I had two babies like this. I changed formula after formula, thinking I was dealing with babies that were allergic to milk. These babies were X-rayed for thymus, and the gastrointestinal tracts were X-rayed. The reports came back normal thymus. The gastrointestinal reports came back showing pyloric spasm, and indicating that I should give a sedative. But I could not see a spasm without some cause for it and a sedative would cover up the cause. And I continued to say to the mother, "If you can't sleep, there is a reason; you are sick or perhaps you are mad with your husband, and a sedative won't cure either trouble."

So I have never used sedatives with little babies but have looked for the cause for the spasm. For a baby to get nicotine, alcohol, caffeine, phenobarbital, or any drug for nine months, and then all of a sudden to be born and the mother not nurse him so that the dissipation is cut off rather than tapered off, makes the baby a nervous wreck until he gets off the drug. To get the baby off the drug takes from three to six months,

I remember a little baby who was brought to my office late one night by a foster mother. He was about one week old. She said he had "cried solid" for one week, which I am sure was an exaggeration for the child had to have some sleep. He had a severe tremor, very stiff hands, and feet cold and blue. His liver was down to the crest of the ileum. His spleen was enlarged. He looked like a case of tetany. I had never seen a baby in that condition before. After getting the history, the cause was quite evident. The mother was an alcoholic who had been drunk most of the time for nine months. By depriving the baby of the large amounts of alcohol he had been receiving, he had developed all the after effects of an alcoholic deprived of alcohol. At the end of one year this child walked, talked, and had developed, but was not a normal child, although he had been cared for and trained by a foster mother who made every effort to give him the best food and training a child could get.

Then there was the little baby who was brought in one night after his parents had made the rounds for two weeks trying to find a doctor who could stop the wakefulness and crying. After getting a good history on the mother, I found she had four grains of phenobarbital daily from the very first of her pregnancy until the baby was born. A doctor had given this baby a quarter grain of phenobarbital to try to

Dissipation

get him to sleep or quiet down with no effect, since he was accustomed to four grains a day. So we decided to let the baby cry until he got off the drug and adjusted his life to a non-drug existence. This sounds bad, but I have found that this is the best method. With the aid of one-half cc. of Betalin Complex with Vitamin C in the muscle once a day for one week, these little ones are helped to get off the drug, which is better than putting them on something else they must learn to live without.

When a woman gets pregnant, she goes to the doctor and he advises her to drink milk so her baby will have good teeth and bones; also, to take iron and vitamins so the baby will be perfect. She believes that the doctor is right in telling her about her baby's getting the calcium, iron, and vitamins, but will not believe her baby gets the alcohol, nicotine, caffeine, or any other harmful drug she takes. Even though mothers refuse to believe this, the fact is true and will take its toll.

Life seems to have grown all too complicated yet, when we think about it, it is just as simple as ever. The natural laws have not changed one iota.

Some days, after working the usual long hours without stopping, trying to help these mothers get their babies straightened out so they can be the pleasure they should be, I look out into the deep forest back of my office and think: how are the mother rabbits and the mother birds going about their job? With no bother, they seem to know just what to do. We may say that is instinct; but as the animal has instinct, mankind has knowledge, wisdom and understanding. If the rabbit with only instinct can bring into life a normal, happy baby, then woman with all her superiority in knowledge, wisdom, and understanding should do a much better job if she but uses these God-given abilities.

A mother will be faithful to drink her quart of milk each day, take her vitamins, iron, and maybe a little extra calcium; yet the cow has a perfect calf without ever drinking a drop of milk or taking any vitamins. Women should think this thing through. It is not the thing the mother does not take, in most cases, that causes her to have an abnormal baby; it is what she does take that destroys the baby's chance to be what he could have been had the mother and father made their bodies as perfect as possible within the scope of their abilities.

In breeding animals, much stress is placed on the male. Thousands of dollars have been paid for a superior bull, horse, or dog. Thus, the quality of the male in the breeding of the lower animals must be very important.

Many times in the breeding of a child, the sperm that is to make a part of that first cell has lived its entire existence in a medium of nicotine, alcohol, and other substances that are detrimental to living protoplasm. When this sperm unites with an ovum that has lived likewise in such a medium and a baby results, that child has been condemned already. If this baby continues to live, from the time he is one cell until he is nine months old, in a medium of nicotine, alcohol, caffeine, we could not expect this child to be normal.

This is the day of the greatest dissipation by women since the beginning of time. There are more things now for a person to take that are harmful to the body than ever before. Each year the number of maladjusted, abnormal children is increasing by leaps and bounds. We can talk to any teacher in any school and he or she will tell us that a relatively small percent of the children in an average class are keeping up without difficulties with the grade for their age. The schools for ungraded children are increasing and juvenile delinquency continues to increase. The mentally as well as the physically handicapped children are increasing.

This should not be, for man has learned much about the human body and how to combat diseases with all the wonderful drugs. He has also increased his understanding of the value of foods. In the animal kingdom we do not see this downgrading, nor do we see an increase in mental and physical abnormality. Yet we see it in human beings in spite of our wonderful drugs and knowledge about immunity.

Children today are not generally the victims of long, debilitating diseases that leave them handicapped. Man knows more about how to make a perfect body today than ever before in history. Yet more human beings, especially helpless babies, are sacrificed on the altar of dissipation than ever before.

In the mill village the mother ate snuff and her daughter in turn got married and she ate snuff; and the little baby she conceived was made from a sperm that came from a man who had chewed tobacco from childhood. We cannot expect a baby from this marriage to rise above his parents.

No social or religious environment or financial help can change these people until they themselves give up the thing that is destroying them. Man has to want to be helped before he can be helped, and if he is born to parents that have made him inferior, the job is difficult.

Today when women smoke until their skin is "cobblestoned" and yellow, their teeth brown, and their breath so bad one can smell them across the room, we cannot expect a normal baby to come out of a body like that. Our children today are superior to those of fifty years ago because they have not had to have whooping cough, scarlet fever that lasted for months, smallpox, typhoid fever, diphtheria, tetanus, and diseases like meningitis. Diarrhoea and pneumonia can be cured in a few hours and this is done so easily the body is not hurt by these one-time killers. So the child that has been fortunate enough to be born of good parents has a far better chance to develop a good body and good mind than the child born of good parents fifty or sixty years ago.

The sad realization that comes to a baby doctor is that the little cuddly, well-born babies are decreasing in number. More of the dissipated type come to me each year,

The advertisements in newspapers and magazines show a beautiful girl by a soft-running brook with a handsome young man, both smoking, and they appear to be having the most wonderful time on earth. It makes us older people long for the flesh pots of Egypt. The girl's teeth are beautiful, her skin is soft and smooth, and she looks like she breathes out the essence of roses. The boy's teeth are snow-white, skin pink and soft. How could any young boy or girl not want this picture of the clean, white smoke rising from a cozy nook?

The devil has always made wrong-doings enticing. He never gives us the picture of this handsome couple after they have smoked for thirty years, or this couple up all night with a baby who has been born addicted to tobacco and now has to do without it. Yes, this condition is increasing all the time, and the tobacco and alcohol companies are happy to publish each year statistics showing how many more fine boys and girls they have started on the road to destruction of the only body they will ever have, the home of the soul.

Mothers come in to me and say, "Doctor, Johnny could pass his work if he would put his mind to it." But poor little Johnny is not to blame for his inability to learn; he was once a real nicotine addict, and not by choice.

Recently, one of these mothers came in with a three weeks old baby whom I heard crying before they reached the office. The maternal grandmother was with them. Although I was very busy, the child was crying so loud and hard, I asked my secretary to bring the baby right in. At a glance I knew what the trouble was. So I had the mother wrap the child tightly and place him on his abdomen. The baby continued to cry. As soon as I could get the table cleared, I had these people brought into the examining room. The young mother was in tears and the grandmother had tried all she knew to get the baby quiet and relaxed but she had failed. The formula had been changed several times; they had tried a little sedation; but the baby continued to jump at the least noise and to scream out when he was moved. His face showed that he was in severe pain, he was stiff as a board, cyanotic, feet and hands cold, and with the least motion I could feel his muscles go into a tonic contraction that must have been very painful.

After finishing the examination, I explained to the mother that it would take a while to get this baby off nicotine and that Vitamin B with C always seemed to help relax such a baby. So the baby was given one cc. Betalin Complex with Vitamin C in the muscle. The mother was instructed to wrap the child tightly, keep him on his abdomen, and put him on a schedule.

The grandmother spoke up and said, "Now I have learned something. My other daughter had a baby about the same time this baby was born, and that baby is as soft and relaxed as a little bunny; they have never had a minute's trouble. That daughter has never used tobacco or coffee."

I remember one mother who brought two sons in for me to talk to about smoking. One was ten, the other nine, and I had had these children as patients from birth. They had started smoking and the mother was all upset. When I saw the oldest boy first, he was one week old. He had cried and spit for three days, or since he had left the hospital, This little fellow was stiff, cyanotic, and could not be cuddled. The mother had smoked, drunk, and consumed great quantities of coffee during the entire pregnancy and she did not want to nurse the baby. So he had to suffer the shock of giving up all of it all at once. We worked with this child and, as time went on, he became more relaxed and the mother showed a little love for him. It is hard to make a mother feel good toward a little baby who cries all the time, cannot be cuddled or comforted, refuses food, spits up and has frequent stools. The mother-child relationship reaches a low ebb, and the child feels it. I have had mother after mother say to me, "This is it; I never want another child; I am a nervous wreck!"

After one and a half years another boy was born to this family and he was worse than the first. He had severe tremor and was tested for everything. All reports came back normal. We really worked on this little baby, trying to get a formula to stay down but it was four months before he began to relax and keep his food. Then any food seemed to be all right, for the trouble was not in the food. Allergy is often blamed for many of these unhappy babies.

These two boys did not do well in school. They were the type who could not sit still or be quiet and could not stay on one subject or project long enough to finish. As I have said before, the mothers always say, "Doctor, he could get his work as well as any other child if he would put his mind on it." But I say these children cannot put their minds on their work like a normal child. Something happened to these little boys that made them different. The same thing happened to the little boys that were in my first school, and the children in the mill village, and to the babies born to the dissipated mothers in the medical clinic.

This mother with the two sons who had the poor start wanted me to teach her sons that they had a selfish, weak mother. I said to the boys, "Your mother wants me to keep you boys from smoking, and that would be just as impossible as it was for her mother to keep her from smoking. Her mother was heartbroken when your mother started smoking and doing things that would destroy her body. Now your mother admits she is so weak and nervous she cannot give up these things. She is heartbroken to see you boys start doing the same thing. I say she could be the mother a boy would be proud of if she really wanted to be, but she loves these things more than she loves you, and you must know that you are second in her life. You can't change that; you can't change anything that has passed. But you can determine for yourselves that from here on out you will never do anything to your minds and bodies that will make them less efficient than they are today.

" . . .the best houses possible"

"You should take these bodies and make out of them the best houses possible with what you have. You have such a short time to live, and you are the ones to say just how happy and well this short time will be. You are the only person on earth who can make yourself decide for good or evil. From this day I would always talk to myself and say, 'Young man, you are my subject, and you are to do what I say and that is to keep this house clean and in the best of health.'

"No, I can't tell you not to do anything. I can tell you what certain things will do to you if you do them, but you must decide what you want in life and go after it. Your mother wants me to put desire and ambition in your life, but this is impossible. That has to come from within. Think these things over and decide for God and not for the devil."

Another interesting case was that of a mother from the Central Presbyterian Church clinic. Her mouth was always filled with snuff or tobacco. She brought her baby in because she could not retain her food and had diarrhoea. The little girl looked terrible. We worked with this child for fourteen years. She was just one of the hundreds of these children who did not look like they were worth saving.

At sixteen she got married. She could not do well in school. The boy she married was a fine young man from the country who had never dissipated, and she had done the best she could with the body she had.

When their baby was born, he was perfect. She nursed him and kept him on a good schedule. At six years this boy has a good mind and body and is as well-adjusted as any child could be. It seems that the sperm and ovum that originate in clean bodies, even though those bodies have been handicapped by their parents, can produce a perfect child.

When we bring in these little unfortunate children to a medical conference to try to determine the cause of their condition and what can be done to solve the trouble, or to correct it, a great deal of money can be spent making tests, both physical and mental. A great doctor who never talked much, but who thought deeply, Dr. William Funkhouser, sometimes made this statement, "These children are made of poor protoplasm." The veterinarian has known about this for years.

One day a father and mother brought three little children for me to check. The mother looked about as bad as a woman could look, and the father even worse. The mother's skin was brown and "cobblestoned" in appearance and her breath was so bad from tobacco you had to hold your breath to talk to her. Her teeth were so brown from tobacco stain that as she smiled, her mouth looked like a dark hole. The father looked the same. I asked them to sit down and then asked the question, "What is your trouble?"

The father spoke up, "Doc, we have had three children and not one of them has been any good. There is something wrong with all three, and I want you to see if you can straighten them out."

I thought to myself: If I had a stallion that looked like that man and a mare that looked like that mother, I would not expect a Kentucky race horse out of their colt. Breeding animals or plants is no different from breeding people. We are spending large sums of money building schools and institutions to take care of these people and nothing trying to teach young people about the importance of the ovum and sperm that will make the child who may have to spend his life as a ward of the state. There are very few colleges now that do not have a smoking room. We are educating the minds of children but destroying their bodies.

Thousands of years ago, Samson's mother and Samuel's mother knew that a pregnant woman should not take wine or dissipate. Yet when we speak to a young mother about her dissipation during pregnancy, she will say that she had no idea her baby would get any of the nicotine, alcohol, or other drugs that she took. A mother must know that all of the drugs that she takes will have their effects upon her baby.

I remember one little baby who was born to a mother who had to take large quantities of a diuretic for the last six months of her pregnancy. Forty-eight hours after her baby was born, he had not urinated, and his skin and muscles became so hard you could not press them in, It looked as though this baby would not live. His electrolytes had been so disturbed that he could not adjust without the drug for a while. At times we see a baby that was given too much sedation while the mother was in labor, or a baby with a tachycardia we cannot explain, which could be due to an overdose of something the mother could take, but the baby could not.

Smoking is one of the most effective methods to reduce or lose weight for, if a person smokes to any appreciable extent, the sense of smell can almost be destroyed. If we cannot smell food, the taste is not there and the interest in food is lost. When a mother smokes during pregnancy, she finds it easy to go without food since the normal pleasure one should get from the wonderful aroma of good food doesn't exist. The sense of smell has a great deal to do with digestion as the digestive juices begin to flow when stimulated by the smell of food. This is very important to the process of digestion. So, if a mother does not have the normal reaction to food, she does not digest it well and the unborn baby will suffer.

I have seen babies in my office from homes where the mother and the father both smoked in a small house in the winter time, and the mucosa in the nose would be so swollen the baby could not breathe through the nose at all, nor would he be able to eat. When these children go on a picnic or spend the day in a home where there is no smoke, they breathe with no trouble and eat well.

I remember one little baby like this who had been treated for a cold for three months. I asked the grandmother to keep him for a week and he breathed normally and ate well until he went back home. There are many such children who are treated for colds and poor appetites that would be well if they had clean air to breathe and good, well-spaced meals.

The damage that is done to a newborn baby from smoke in the room is greater than many people realize. One such baby we let sleep in a car just outside the mother's window, some have slept on porches to obtain relief, and we have sent some to the hospitals so the parents could see how well they do when away from smoke.

One little boy had eczema so badly he was oozing literally from head to foot. We put him in the hospital on the same diet, and no medicine. He cleared up but soon after he got home, the eczema came back. We tried this child on the beach, in the mountains, but found nothing would clear up his skin and keep it clear except to stay away from tobacco smoke.

One may say it would have been simpler to have the mother and father give up tobacco, No, that is the hardest job I have ever tried. Smoking seems to mean more to many parents than their children's food, health, or education. I don't know how many babies I have seen hungry and without clothes, whose mothers and fathers were chain smokers. Love for children operates in strange ways in some people. In some cases, love is what the parents give if it does not cost them anything.

Another interesting case was that of a little boy who was brought in for diagnosis, He was five years old and had never talked or seemed to understand speech. He crouched like a cat behind objects, and could not be controlled. His body was small but he could hear and see, and he walked well. He was studied by all the doctors in the hospital.

The psychiatrist seemed to think he had a rejection complex, but no explanation was found for this condition. When a good history of the mother was taken, it was found that she had spent the entire nine months in the hospital with pernicious vomiting and most of the time was nourished through the veins. No one would have to go beyond this to know why this little boy was so handicapped. He was starved for nine months. This boy had a brother who was born two years later who was normal. The mother was not sick with this pregnancy.

One of the boys at the clinic was another interesting case. This boy had always seemed to be a maniac from birth. His body was small, but on physical examination there appeared to be nothing abnormal. He had cried from birth as though he were frightened. He was always destroying everything he came near. He never talked, but had a cry like a wild animal. This child went the rounds of all the clinics and doctors, and at nine years he was sent to a mental hospital. This child's mother was a morphine addict. She had had morphine a long time before pregnancy, and during the pregnancy the damage was done. The damage done to this child seemed to have been neurological, as is the case with nicotine and caffeine.

The sperm and ovum have certain innate characteristics that cannot be changed, such as color, mental powers, stature, number of teeth, color of hair, number of toes, color of eyes, and hundreds of other things produced when these cells combine. What everyone should be taught is that, above all, these cells should be nourished and protected from anything that is harmful to living protoplasm so that the innate characteristics in them can develop and go into the making of a body and mind that can function at maximum capacity and efficiency.

Only recently I had a fifteen-year-old boy in my office. He was tall, flabby, every tooth in his head rotted off, skin covered with pustules, sad face, long hair combed like a misfit's. The mother said he would not eat, and from birth had literally lived on carbonated drinks, at least four a day. I thought to myself, how could a parent destroy a child so completely? What was this child the day he was conceived? What were his possibilities? We just cannot afford to do one thing that will destroy a child's chance in life. In this most wonderful country of ours what a great waste of human potential we see!

When a pregnancy is diagnosed, the mother should be given a thorough examination to be sure she is in good physical condition. She should then be instructed to eat a balanced diet and to be sure not to breathe, rub on her skin, or otherwise consume anything that she would not want her baby to get. Many women look upon pregnancy as an illness and take all kinds of medicine and eat a special diet at this time. No medicine is needed if the woman is in good health, nor is a special diet required. She should be told that if she dissipates, her baby will suffer.

Milk Anemia

The quart of milk once thought to be necessary for a pregnant mother is a big mistake. Milk in large quantities causes anemia and, if a mother consumes a quart of milk a day, she will get anemic in a very short time and the baby will not get the oxygen he needs. If milk were important to make perfect babies, I am sure nature would have provided some way for the mothers of the lower animals to get milk during their pregnancy.

We can feed a chicken or turkey milk for a short time and there will be no dark meat; it is all white meat. The bird is so anemic it does not have enough blood to make the more vascular parts of the body dark when cooked. No other animal except the human takes milk during pregnancy. Oxygen is of the utmost importance to the fetus and, if the mother is anemic, the fetus must suffer. As the fetus develops, it has to develop more red cells than normal to try to take up as much oxygen as possible. This great demand on the blood-forming organs of the fetus may have much to do with anemia of early babyhood. After delivery, with his high hemoglobin and a normal atmosphere of oxygen, the demand for making red cells would not exist.

Uncontrolled diabetes has a great influence on the baby that is being formed. Ninety percent of the Mongoloid children I have had in my practice have come from mothers who have a scar on the neck or who say they could not get pregnant until the doctor started them on thyroid. Just what the relationship is, I do not know; but it seems too frequent to be coincidental.

Young people must be taught that if they marry short mates, they may have short children; if they marry tall mates, their children may be tall; if they marry fat mates, their children may be fat; if the mate is black, brown, yellow, the outcome may be the same; and if they marry mates who dissipate, they may have the products that come from this condition. A young person should look over the prospective mate and his or her parents before getting married and ask himself or herself this most important question: Will I be willing to accept a child of as good or as bad quality as that stored in the cell that will make my child?

Accepting Children for What They Are

The unaccepted child is one of our greatest problems. He is too tall, too short, too light, too dark, too active, too slow, too smart, too dumb, hair too red, too white or too black. Much of this dissatisfaction and so-called disappointment would be eliminated if we would teach our children and young people that we get apples off apple trees, and we get children from the parents that make them.

We cannot expect to make a silk purse out of a pig's ear, but we can take a pig's ear and make a pigskin purse; and we must be willing to accept the pigskin purse. Every day in my office the complaint comes about some little child that cannot help how he was born, but the mother has her plans to make a silk purse out of a pig's ear and, if she can't, she will destroy the pig's ear by continually talking about how heartbroken she is with the child she has that she made.

We must be willing to accept the child that does not have the looks, the stature, or the mental ability that we want in the same way we accept the blind. They are here and we cannot make them over. What they are mentally and physically has already been determined. But we can take what we have and develop it to capacity. Nobody knows how many children, big and little, are heartbroken because of their parents' continual nagging and dissatisfaction with the fact that the children are what they are and not what the parents want.

If a child is handicapped by the way he was made, three great forces may make this child improve and have a useful and happy life: parents, religion, and psychiatry. Many times women and men are born of normal parents who did everything in their power to make them as perfect as possible and to give them every chance to develop, yet these people marry and start dissipating so that the child brought into the world by them cannot do as well as they did. The problem begins when the parents start telling the child how inferior he is, or that he is not really trying, and to criticize him generally. Soon the teacher starts to talk about his lack of interest.

This child is forced to go to school and to compete with the children who are well born. and has to answer up in class before boys and girls who laugh at his moronic answers. Soon the child either shrinks back and will not be seen, or he does something physical to show that if he does not have the power to keep up mentally, he can do something physical to get recognition. And eventually many of these young people are labelled juvenile delinquents.

This was not the case many years ago. Different types of people went to school with their own types. The mill village children went to a school in a mill village, the farm children to a school in the country, and the city children to a school in the city. The moron could stay out of school and do the work he was capable of doing in his own home or with his own type. If he could not keep up, he did not have to be laughed at or shuttled about from one school to another.

If parents and teachers could approach this problem with the same amount of understanding and kindness as they do the problem of the blind or the deaf child, it would help. The types of children we have discussed are just as truly handicapped as are the blind or the deaf. These children who cannot adjust, or who cannot keep up mentally or physically with their age group are just as truly unfortunate as any other handicapped child, and they should be led to understand that, with the help of God, they can and must take the lives they have and make a blessing out of them. Parents and teachers must be willing to say to these children, "If you cannot learn mathematics, you can learn to drive a nail or to dig a ditch. You cannot be blamed for your condition, and you can take what you have and be happy. You don't have to run if your legs are off."

We must teach and reteach parents the importance of a child's being well born, and that there is nothing on earth as important as the making of a new life.

Some time ago a mother was in my office with a little girl, and this mother had been doing something that was very harmful to her child. I said to her, "Why don't you give this up?" and this was her answer, "But, Doctor, I like to do that!" How could any mother on earth like to do something that would hurt a little child who did not ask to come into that home?

Handicapped children should be taught that they are just as im-

portant in the sight of God as the smartest child in the class, and
that no more is required of them than they are able to do. No boy
or girl ever became a juvenile delinquent until somebody made a
nobody out of him or her. Parents, teachers, and preachers should
never run them down or tell them how inferior they are, or make a
nobody out of them. When a child is made to feel he is a nobody, he
quits trying, and the road down is easy, for that is what is expected
of him. Many of these children could be saved if their parents would
be willing to do what is best for them and give up the things that
handicap them.

The mother quoted above wants her child to be like the child next
door, whose mother might have liked the harmful things she was
doing, but who loved her child enough to deprive herself to see that
he had a chance. But this cannot be until she decides to put her child
first in her life.

A fine child is pay enough for any sacrifice a parent can make.

The religious approach to this problem is one way. Also the psychiatric approach, if we can separate these two, may help. These two
methods in reality are the same, but may be expressed differently.
The psychiatrist can bring these people to see that the standards set
up whereby man's importance is judged are in many instances
wrong. It is not true that the only important people are the educated
and the rich, but man is just as important as he thinks he is. So the
psychiatrist can show the child that he does not have to steal, kill,
drink, smoke, drive too fast, or hate to get recognition.

Thomas Jefferson made the statement that all men are created
equal. This is not true today, for thousands of little children are condemned by their parents before they are born. The answer to the
problem is not in better schools, better playgrounds, or better environment, but is in better parents.

Many children are lost in the first few hours of life, and a major
cause of this is that they are born prematurely. We know that nicotine causes uterine contraction, and at the right time in the men-
strual cycle, from the time of conception to the time of delivery,
anything that would increase these contractions could cause miscar-
riage or premature delivery. There are many reasons for premature
deliveries but, if we would cut down on nicotine, we could reduce
the number of premature births and save many babies. Premature
babies have a stormy time at best.

To repeat, I wonder what our suffragette friend would say if she would come back today and see just what we women have done with our emancipation. Women should never have been deprived of a human right, but with freedom comes responsibility. No woman, no race, no country should be free until they are able to use freedom to better themselves and mankind. We will not turn a child out of our homes until he is able to make his own way in the world and to use his freedom from parental domination intelligently enough to establish a home and a life of his own. Freedom is a dangerous thing if the free person has no feeling or thought of his fellow man.

Has our emancipation brought man up to a higher level of right living, or has woman lowered her standards and lost all she was fighting for? If the women who worked so hard and gave their lives to get the right to vote could come back today and see what has happened to women in the last sixty years, how would they feel? In some things they would be happy. Women have made great contributions to the physical, chemical, and spiritual world with this freedom. But we have with us those who use their freedom to make others slaves. I am sure these women who made the great fight for freedom would be heartbroken to see how many have used their freedom. These women were sure they would give little children a better chance, and the children of today who are blessed with parents who care are better than any other children that have ever lived, for they are not crippled or destroyed by sickness and poor diet. But these children are becoming the minority group.

Recently, I had an invitation to a meeting of the most intellectual women of our town, and the invitation read like this: "There will be a Social Hour from six to seven o'clock, then dinner. After dinner one of our group will speak on the Evils of Alcoholism." It may be that not one of these women was born of dissipated parents, but now they have passed into a man's world and they have so-called man's rights. They are seriously trying to make a better world, but they are trying to begin on the outside, on the other people, where the forces against them are so great. With all of their knowledge and influence, they should begin on their own lives, and with all the power that is in them live the life of the perfect mother, the perfect doctor, the perfect lawyer, or perfect dentist. Women make or break a home, a nation, or a world, and we must come back to the importance of the individual if we are to save America. Every woman should take her life as the starting place to make a better world to live in. We can't put this over at meetings, or by building places to constrain and restrain.

A news item in an Atlanta paper some time ago stated that our mayor had made a gift of a substantial amount of money to one of our psychiatric clinics to study alcoholism. How wonderful if that money could be spent teaching young people that man is free, and that man does what he wants to do, and that if he is an alcoholic, he drinks because he likes to drink, and that he is the one to decide if he is to be cured or not. Man cannot be helped unless he wants to be helped. We can find all kinds of excuses for our behavior, but God and the law hold each person responsible for his acts. Man is free to act, and this freedom is a blessing to some and a curse to others.

It was a large enough problem for society when only the lowest class dissipated, but today the so-called better class and the most intellectual make up a large portion of the people who are dissipating and are not giving their children as good a chance as was given to them.

I can't help thinking that perhaps freedom for women has been a little too much for us and that maybe after women have shown men that they can do everything a man can do, we will come to ourselves and realize that the only way for this country of ours to go up instead of down will be for every woman in America to take her freedom and make of herself a true example of what she wants her child to be.

As it is, we are certain to get increasing numbers of neurologically damaged children. If one could observe one of these little babies a few hours after he is born and see the hard, contracted muscles, and his pain on being disturbed, his sickness, the spitting of milk, the cold and blue feet, he would understand how upset the parents feel when they find that there is no immediate help for that child and that he cannot even be consoled or cuddled. A child of this type has been deprived of his birthright, the right to be born under the most favorable circumstances possible with a chance to develop to highest capacity.

We must teach children that God did not make them blind, deaf, tall, short, white, brown, black, dumb, or wise; but that all of this was given them by physical man. Therefore God must not be blamed for these physical defects every time they occur, but that God can help them make a blessing out of what they have.

♂ ♀

A general summation

I am sure the average reader will have seen by now that I have strong convictions on a number of matters that directly affect a child, the born and the unborn. Once a child is conceived, which is not of his or her choosing but, except in the case of rape, is a wilful act of a male and female, the child should be permitted to grow and be nurtured normally in the mother's womb until delivery and, in my opinion, any adverse interference with this routine is contrary to the laws of our creator.

In several chapters of the book I have commented on a number of things that are harmful to the fetus during the pregnancy period and will increase the probability that the child will be born with physical handicaps he may not be able to overcome. Based on my many years of experience I would put at the head of the list of those things that are harmful smoking and the use of alcoholic beverages. When a pregnant woman smokes or drinks her unborn child smokes and drinks also and one of the saddest experiences in my practice is to see a tiny newborn that is addicted to nicotine or alcohol. Some of the procedures that can be followed that will help such babies are mentioned previously and will not be repeated here. Suffice it to say that if the mother left off the smoking her child would have a better chance to grow and develop into a normal person. As smoking and drinking affect the fetus so do the use of drugs and improper dieting habits. My suggestion to every woman who finds herself pregnant is that she have a frank talk with her obstetrician and get his advice as to how she should conduct herself during her pregnancy. I sincerely believe that every normal woman deep down in her heart wants her baby to be normal and, if properly advised, will give up during pregnancy any bad habits she may have formed, such as smoking, drinking, and using drugs. We can not over-emphasize the importance of a good start in the life of a baby and that start begins at conception.

A newborn child is perhaps the most helpless of all creatures. He or she is the best example I know of total dependency. Our Creator instilled into the breast of woman what we refer to as "mother love" and this comes to a climax in the birth of a child. It is natural that her child should come first with her and the child is fortunate when this is the case. I have strong feelings on the importance of close mother-child relationships during the formative or early years of a child's life. A child should be trained by his mother and father, a job that cannot be delegated to others except at the child's loss.

The best way to teach a child is by example and fortunate is the child who is reared by upright God-fearing parents who not only tell him how to live but show him. In the two-room country school I attended as a child (my husband attended the same school) one of the subjects we studied was physiology. In this study we learned that some substances taken into our bodies were harmful and should be avoided. Among these were alcohol, tobacco, and some drugs. The older I get and the more experience I have as a physician the more conscious I am of the truth contained in the little physiology book we used as a text. Children should be taught by their parents that they should not eat, drink, or use anything that might be injurious to their health and the parents can add weight to their teaching by living up to the standards they recommend for their children. If my husband and I had smoked or used alcohol I don't think our daughter would have been too much impressed by any suggestion we might have made that she should not smoke or drink. After children become adults they are on their own and can and must make their own decisions. During the childhood years the parents have the grave responsibility of doing all they can through advice and by example to steer them in the right direction. Truly every child should have a chance to go to the top in keeping with his talents and capabilities.